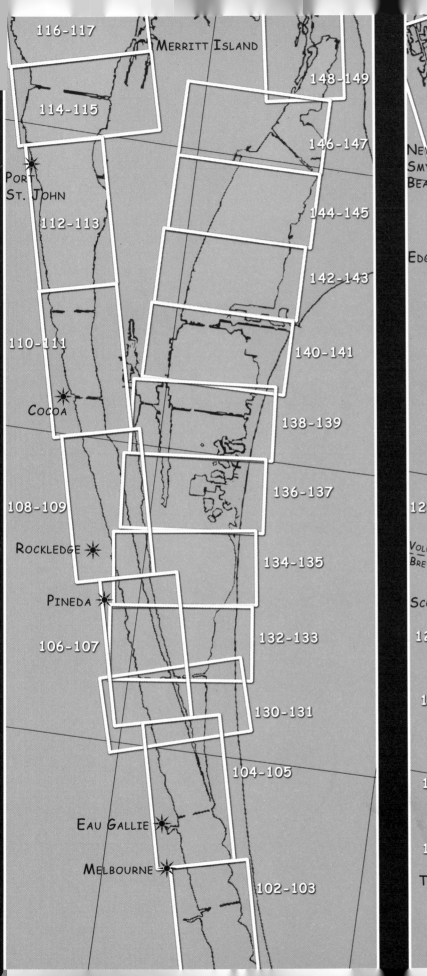
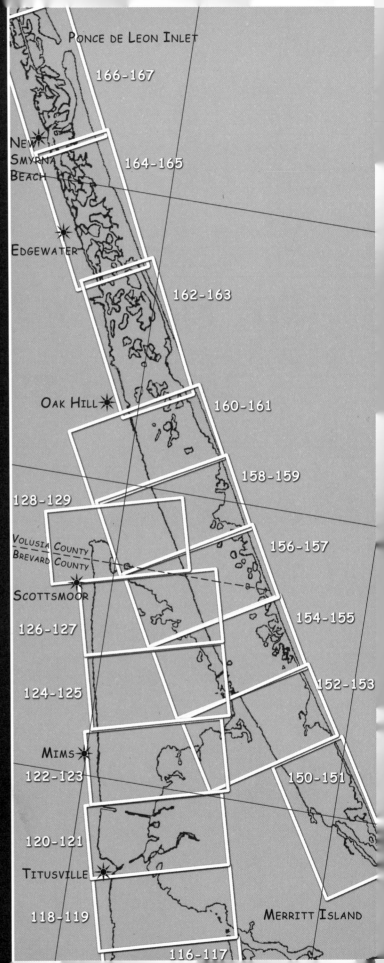

Waterways & Byways of the Indian River Lagoon

Field Guide for Boaters, Anglers & Naturalists

Mark Masterton Littler &
Diane Scullion Littler

OffShore Graphics, Inc.

First published 2003 by OffShore Graphics, Inc.
First Printing October, 2003

Library of Congress Control Number: 2003095651
Cataloging Data

Littler, Mark Masterton
Waterways & Byways of the Indian River Lagoon / Mark Masterton Littler, Diane Scullion Littler
ISBN 0-9678901-4-4
1. Fishing—Indian River Lagoon—Identification. 2. Fish—Indian River Lagoon—Pictorial Works. 3. Shorebirds—Indian River Lagoon—Pictorial Works. 4. Aerial Photography—Indian River Lagoon—Pictorial Works. 5. Marine Organisms—Indian River Lagoon. 6. Marine Biology.
I. Diane Scullion Littler. II. Title.

Published and distributed by:
    OffShore Graphics, Inc.
    P.O. Box 6139
    Washington, D.C. 20044-6139, U.S.A.

Printed in China on acid free paper through:
    Phoenix Offset
    (No. 8) Industrial Bldg.
    20 Wang Hoi Road
    Kowloon Bay, Hong Kong

Color production by:
    Asia Pacific Offset, Inc.
    1332 Corcoran Street NW, #6
    Washington, D.C. 20009, U.S.A.

DISCLAIMER

The intended purpose of this field guide is to inform and entertain. The authors and OffShore Graphics, Inc. shall have no liability or responsibility to any individual or group of individuals for losses or damages caused, directly or indirectly, by the information contained in this book, including any typographical or factual errors. All maps and aerial photographs in this field guide are for general information and are not intended for navigation. It is recommended that updated NOAA and USCG navigational charts be obtained and used for navigational purposes.

CONTENTS

Looking eastward from Fort Pierce across Taylor Creek and North Bridge (A1A) toward the intricate mangrove island byways bordering North Hutchison Island.

ACKNOWLEDGEMENTS

The majority of information on IRL habitats was obtained from our own research, a useful summary series of Florida Fish and Wildlife Conservation Commission (FWC) articles and brochures (found at www.marinefisheries.org) and the scientific literature. The 1992 book, "Ecosystems of Florida", edited by Ronald Myers and John Ewel (University of Central Florida Press, Orlando), was the main source of summary knowledge on IRL mangrove, salt marsh, seagrass, impoundment, oyster bar and algal communities. The aerial photographs (HAS Images, Inc.) were chartered by the St. Johns River Water Management District (SJRWMD). The outstanding fish illustrations are dry brush watercolors by Diane Rome Peebles of St. Petersburg, Florida, and have been reproduced courtesy of FWC: 2001. Fishing Lines, Angler's Guide to Florida Marine Resources, 4th edition, Jason Schratwieser (editor), Division of Marine Fisheries. This last publication shares similar goals to those of this book; enabling sportsmen to accurately identify the IRL's predominant regulated fishes and other wildlife and to encourage modern boating/ angling protocols and ethics. Data on fishes were gleaned from www.fishbase.org; whereas, much of the shorebird data were extracted from www.enature.com. The Florida fishing records, quoted from the FWC website, are provided only as benchmarks, since they are continually changing. The common names of fish are those cited in the American Fisheries Society book, "Common and Scientific Names of Fishes".

We particularly appreciate the expertise and help of Robert Virnstein (SJRWMD), who has been dedicated to understanding IRL seagrass and invertebrate ecosystems for over two decades. Ned Smith (Harbor Branch Oceanographic Institution, HBOI) kindly provided unpublished information on tidal circulation phenomena. Becky Robbins (South Florida Water Management District) made informative comments on the initial draft and gave valuable insights into the status of IRL seagrasses, from the perspective of one who closely monitors grass beds in the field. We also thank Kathy Hill for reviewing the first draft of the introduction. Dennis Hanisak (HBOI) provided a thoughtful critique of the final draft. Sherry Reed's assistance was instrumental in locating specific IRL fauna and flora. The good fisher-folks at White's Tackle Shop in Fort Pierce advised us on which of the many IRL fish species warranted inclusion. Hewes Light Tackle Boats and Lindsay Marine of Stewart facilitated our purchase of a Bonefisher Skiff that made accessing the IRL backcountry a pleasure. All photographs are by Diane Littler, with the following exceptions courtesy of: Barbara Brown (p. 18), Don Hurlbert (below), Peggy Lento (p. 15), Gini Locke (p. 6, top) and Jeff Tinsley (inside back jacket).

Foremost, we have attempted to feature informative overviews, personal insights and useful tools—such as the fish, bird, mammal and plant identification sections and the overflight photographs. These will enable naturalists to increase their knowledge of the interconnected ecosystems of the IRL, as well as to encourage boating activities to be spread farther and wider afield. It is our sincerest hope that this field guide to the intricate waterways and hidden byways of the Indian River Lagoon will motivate interested boaters, anglers and naturalists to become consummate students and advocates of the incredible biota and diverse array of habitats of this remarkable resource. HBOI Contribution No. 1524 and SMSFP Contribution No. 568.

INTRODUCTION

PHYSICAL CHARACTERISTICS

The Indian River Lagoon (IRL) spans more than one-third of Florida's east coast, extending 156 miles from its southern limit at Jupiter Inlet (north of Palm Beach) to Ponce de Leon Inlet (south of Daytona Beach). The Indian River Lagoon System actually consists of three lagoons: 1) the Indian River (spanning the northeast tip of Palm Beach County and nearly the entire coastal lengths of Martin, St. Lucie, Indian River and Brevard Counties, with its northern tip in Volusia County), 2) the Banana River (entirely within Brevard County) and 3) the Mosquito Lagoon (which extends from Brevard County to northern Volusia County). It ranks as both the longest saltwater estuary in Florida and the most extensive barrier-island/tidal-inlet system in the United States. The geological development of the IRL began prior to 10,000 years ago when southward flowing currents deposited massive quantities of silica based sands, that had eroded from the southern Appalachians, onto the continental shelf off eastern Florida. The IRL subsequently formed when sea level rise began to slow (around 6,000 years ago) and the previously submerged sand bars became exposed and stabilized as barrier islands. It connects to the Atlantic Ocean through five different inlets (Jupiter, St. Lucie, Fort Pierce, Sebastian and Ponce de Leon) associated with river mouths that provide significant, but sporadic, freshwater pulses. Paralleling the coastline, the IRL and its many estuaries are almost landlocked between the widespread inlets, particularly the two northernmost which are almost 90 miles apart. Today's IRL marine plant and animal communities have developed throughout the past 3,000 years under rapidly changing geological and oceanographic conditions.

The Indian River Lagoon spans a transitional area between subtropical and warm-temperate zones (from 26°N, 80°W to 29°N, 81°W) and overlaps a well documented biogeographical boundary, including the temperate Carolinian Province in the north, while being exposed to tropical organisms carried by currents from the Caribbean, Gulf and Antilles Provinces to the south. The dominant features of the IRL are its structurally complex plant communities (mangrove forests, salt marshes, seagrass flats, algal beds) as well as oyster reefs, rock/gravel hard-bottoms and mud/sand soft-bottoms. The intermingling of both warm- and cold-water species, along with a mosaic of structurally diverse shoreline and submerged community types, have contributed to the IRL being recognized as the most biologically diverse estuarine system in the continental United States. To date, roughly 4,000 different kinds of plants and animals have been recorded within the boundaries of the IRL (over 1,000 plants and about 3,000 animals, including more than 400 fishes and 300 birds). It would also seem likely that ballast waters and fouling organisms from the considerable shipping and recreational boating activities have been a further source of foreign marine life (Australian Spotted Jellyfish, Indo-Pacific Swimming Crab, Striped Barnacle).

The Indian River Lagoon is quite shallow with an average depth of only about 6 feet. It varies in width from less than 0.3 mile at Hobe Sound to 5 miles wide in the northern region near Mosquito Lagoon. Tidal amplitudes, current speeds and oceanic exchanges are almost nonexistent in much of the northern basin and generally increase southward. Tidal currents, which greatly affect water quality, channel depth and salinity, are substantial within several miles of each inlet. In these regions, current speeds during maximum ebb- and flood-stages can exceed 3.5 miles per hour due to the constricting effects of narrow inlet channels and their bordering rip-rap extensions. Tidal exchange periods (complete flushing) average from about one week in the southern Indian River to more than one year in the northern basin, where strong winds frequently move large volumes of surface waters that help mix the system. Jupiter Inlet provides excellent flushing/exchange and some of the best water quality to the IRL. However, its effect does not extend much farther north than the Hobe Sound region, owing to the long and narrow connection to the St. Lucie Inlet. On the other hand, Fort Pierce Inlet provides most (50%) of the overall Indian River's flushing, followed by St. Lucie Inlet (30%) and Sebastian Inlet (20%). Flushing/exchange from Ponce de Leon Inlet's tidal currents is limited to only the northern Mosquito Lagoon. Salt concentrations near the inlets are typically oceanic (35 parts per thousand salt), whereas salinities elsewhere in the lagoon are highly variable as a function of seasonal patterns of freshwater influx and evaporation (average = 25–27 ppt).

Many fishes that spawn offshore use the Indian River Lagoon as a nursery ground. Among these, mullet, Redfish, Tarpon and various snappers and groupers spend their lives from juveniles to adults within the IRL, but move offshore to spawn. For example, the Brown Shrimp is an invertebrate that uses the IRL as a nursery, but spawns in offshore waters. After the fertilized eggs develop offshore, the larvae migrate back and are transported into the IRL estuary by tides and currents. Another prime example is the Striped Mullet, whose offspring that survive the hazardous journey from spawning locations at the edge of the Gulfstream, quickly disperse into salt marshes, muddy tidal creeks and grassy shallows. Mullet are high energy fish, growing rapidly on a diet of algae and decaying vegetation to provide a major cornerstone of the IRL's food web. Mullet, along with shrimp, support all recreational fisheries, as well as most species of shorebirds and the Bottle-Nosed Dolphin.

Economically, the Indian River Lagoon ranks as one of the most important navigational and recreational waterways in the US. Its commercial and recreational interests are responsible for tens of thousands of jobs, generating over a quarter billion dollars in yearly salaries. Fishing activities along the IRL yield an additional $140 million. Boating, fishing, water sports, waterfowl hunting and tourism contribute another half a billion dollars annually. Real estate ventures (about $825 million in annual revenues) and citrus agriculture (a whopping $2 billion) dominate all other economic venues. These last two overpowering interests pose a daunting challenge to preservation of the remaining natural environmental integrity of the Indian River Lagoon.

MANGROVES

Since prehistory, mangrove forests have constituted one of Florida's most important native plant communities. Mangrove(s) is a general term used to describe a broad group of unrelated tropical and subtropical trees and shrubs that share the capacity to thrive in saline environments. Mangroves have the ability to grow well in either freshwater or saltwater. However, they are largely confined to estuaries and upland fringe areas that are periodically flooded by saline waters. The main reason is due to competition for space from the more dominant freshwater vascular plants. By growing in saline waters, as well as oxygen depleted soils, mangroves evade competitive pressures. Mangroves in the IRL live a precarious existence, because of climatic fluctuations, and tend to be much smaller (less than 30 feet high) than their tropical counterparts. Only scattered stands of mangroves are found north of Brevard County, due to winter cold spells, where they are replaced by salt marsh cord grasses. In the Mosquito Lagoon, cord grasses give way to Saltwort and Glasswort marshes, which dominate many of the islands.

The IRL mangrove community consists of three species: the Red, Black and White Mangroves (see pp. 61–62 for descrip-tions). The Buttonwood is a mangrove associate that lacks the structural features characteristic of true mangrove species, but commonly inhabits the upland fringe of many shoreline communities. Buttonwoods are usually shrubby (under 15 feet tall) with lance-shaped alternately-arranged leaves.

About 8,000 acres of mangrove forests line the Indian River Lagoon with a lush and protective border that, along with salt marsh grasses and seagrasses, stabilizes sediments, nurtures diverse and abundant marine invertebrates and shelters juvenile fishes. Birds, including cormorants, pelicans, ibis, egrets, frigates and herons, all use mangrove trees for nesting, foraging and shelter. Mangroves filter the runoff and tidal waters by removing suspended particles and dissolved fertilizers. Mangrove shorelines also buffer inland areas from storm waves and tidal erosion. In fact, mangrove thickets offer so much protection from the elements that boaters facing the threat of hurricanes frequently moor their vessels far up the mangrove creeks for shelter. Early settlers to Florida used salt encrusted Black Mangrove leaves to flavor soups, and prepared the bark to make a tea that was used to repel mosquitoes, treat ulcers and as an antitumor concoction. The tannins extracted from the bark of all three mangrove species, as well as Buttonwoods, were used extensively to preserve leather. Up to 95% of commercially valuable fishes in south Florida spend part of their lives in mangrove habitats.

Red Mangroves are the trees most often encountered by boaters and dominate the shoreline from the upper to the lower intertidal zones. They are distinguished from other mangroves by their reddish prop roots arching out from the

Florida Aligator cruising the mangrove backwaters. The smothering green sheets of Sea Lettuce (Ulva, Enteromorpha) seen clinging to the mangrove roots indicate less than optimal, overly-enriched, nutrient conditions

Prop roots of the Red Mangrove provide critical underwater habitat for invertebrates, baitfish and juvenile gamefish.

Juvenile Snook, jacks, snappers, Sheepshead, grouper, leaflike juvenile Tripletail, 'baby' Goliath Grouper (Jewfish is the politically incorrect former name) and herons hide and forage throughout the tangles of roots. The submerged prop- and aerial-roots serve as substrates for sponges, oysters, mussels, colonial filter feeders and seaweeds. The dense columns of prop roots and their epiphytes shelter and feed countless small baitfishes. Snook and Tarpon cruise the channels and undercut banks just outside the mangrove fringe, on the prowl for the abundant schools of anchovies, herrings and sardines that favor this zone. Young Barracudas and snappers hang among the suspended roots waiting in ambush (p. 8). **Human predators in skinny-water skiffs glide silently among mangrove backwater islands, creeks and shorelines, pin-pointing pockets far under the overhanging branches with surface plugs or flies.** Snook, Spotted Seatrout, Great Barracuda and Tarpon launch themselves from hidden lairs and explode on top water tackle in a burst of shimmering spray.

main trunk or suspended vertically from the branches. Because they have the ability to continually 'tiptoe' seaward (see above), they are the pioneer colonizing species. Red Mangroves can attain heights of 100 feet, with the upper surfaces of leaves being bright glossy green and paler underneath. The abundant hanging propagules of the Red Mangrove are foot-long pencil-like plantlets.

Black Mangroves are found near the mean high water line behind the fringing Red Mangroves, where they may reach 65 feet in height. The leaves of Black Mangroves tend to be dull green, elliptical, bluntly pointed and somewhat narrower than those of Red Mangroves and are often encrusted with salt. They are readily recognized by their gnarled fingerlike aerial roots that emerge from the muck all around the base of the trunk. The Black Mangroves, although less picturesque than the Red Mangroves, also stabilize valuable sedimentary habitat. Their propagules resemble large lima beans.

White Mangroves are more prominent at the highest high-water level, typically growing inland of both Red and Black Mangroves. White Mangroves are significantly shorter than either Red or Black Mangroves, reaching no more than 50 feet tall. Their oval leaves are yellow-green with notched tips; in addition, there are a pair of distinguishing glands at the base. White Mangroves have small mostly underground roots. Their propagules are enclosed in a wrinkled cover and about the size of a pear-shaped sunflower seed.

As the parts of all mangrove trees, marsh grasses and seagrasses die and decay, they contribute organic matter (marine compost) to the food chain. This material is consumed by microorganisms such as bacteria and fungi that break down plant litter to provide food for animals such as sea urchins, crabs, mullet, snails, worms and various crustaceans.

MOSQUITO CONTROL IMPOUNDMENTS

Although mangroves presently total about 8,000 acres throughout the vast Indian River Lagoon, only 1,900 acres (24%) have been available to aquatic life because of impoundments constructed between 1954 and the 1970's. Mosquito control impoundments are areas of salt marshes or mangrove forests that have been surrounded by dikes to allow control of water levels. The location of these extensive impoundments and access roads are clearly revealed in the aerial photographs. **For wade fishers who don't mind hiking-in, the reward is solitude and undisturbed fish populations remote from boat traffic.** The same conditions that make mangroves and marshes optimal for invertebrates and juvenile fish—rich nutrients and shelter—also make them prime salt marsh mosquito breeding grounds. To control the mosquitoes, which require moist mud surfaces to reproduce, the mangroves and marshes were blocked off and flooded. These mosquito abatement techniques successfully facilitated the explosive expansion of the human population along the Treasure and Space Coasts. Unfortunately, the combination of dike construction and waterfront development since the 1940's has severely impacted the majority (50,000 acres, 84%) of the IRL's original mangrove communities.

Although impoundments proved to be an effective method of controlling mosquito populations, there were severe environmental consequences of isolating wetlands from their adjacent estuaries. Some fisheries were greatly affected by the closed impoundments, with significant reductions in invertebrate, baitfish and gamefish species (particularly Snook) that utilized the formerly accessible salt marshes and mangrove forests. Redfish, Tarpon, Ladyfish, Common Snook, mullet and other important commercial and recreational fishes are just a few examples that were adversely affected by closed impoundments. Consequently, 6,100 acres (76%) of the IRL's remaining mangrove forests ceased to be ecologically relevant.

A breakthrough impoundment management strategy for 11,000 acres in St. Lucie , Indian River and Brevard Counties involves flooding to the minimum levels (spillway controlled) needed to prevent egg laying by salt marsh mosquitoes, and only during the summer breeding season. Throughout the remainder of the year (October to May), mechanical culverts installed through the dikes allow for lowering of spillways to further increase flushing by tides. Some of the impoundment culverts are now kept completely open year round, with simultaneous in-and-out circulation, aeration and mosquito abatement. **When flood tides are running, many of the culvert systems produce sufficient current speeds to wash out 'honey holes' that concentrate both baitfish and gamefish, providing little known angling sites.** This management strategy has proven to be an effective procedure for controlling mosquitoes, while greatly improving the salinity, water quality and food balance in both the impoundments and the lagoon. It also helps to retain Black Mangroves, Saltwort, Glasswort and other important native vegetation, as well as allowing the return of millions of transitory fishes such as juvenile Snook and countless invertebrates to nursery grounds previously unavailable to them. Tragically, most of

It is difficult to find a better action gamefish than Bluefish to hook a young lady angler on fishing.

the 27,000 acres of impoundments within the Merritt Island National Wildlife Refuge still remain isolated by dikes and cutoff from the mutually nourishing waters of the IRL.

SEAGRASS COMMUNITIES

Conspicuously abundant and often dominant, seagrasses form vast meadows in sandy or silty shallows. While wading or drifting over shallow flats, you probably have observed gracefully undulating seagrass blades. It is astounding how few boaters or naturalists are informed about these life sustaining systems. Owing to the unsurpassed ecological importance of Indian River Lagoon seagrass meadows and their intricate connections to all of the fisheries as well as to the 'charismatic megafauna', **interested boaters, anglers and naturalists need to become 'students' of this dynamic flats ecosystem.** For that reason, we delve into the fascinating biology of seagrass communities in considerable detail under this section of the guide.

The most luxurious and spatially complex seagrass beds occur in clear shallow waters and, like mangroves and marshes, serve as habitats and nursery grounds for juvenile and

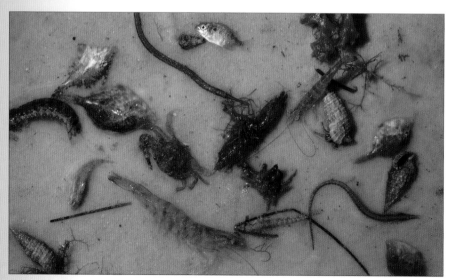

Push net collection of invertebrates (Mud and Brown Shrimp, Hermit, Decorator and Blue Crabs) and fish (Filefish, Pinfish and Pipefish) from a meadow of mixed Turtle and Manatee Grasses.

adult stages of a myriad of epiphytes, invertebrates, fishes, birds and mammals. Seagrass flats are the feeding grounds of some of the most sought-after sport fishes (e.g., Redfish, Tarpon, Bonefish and Permit), and this high-dollar catch-and-release fishery provides an attractive tourism incentive to marine resource managers worldwide. Seagrasses and associated algae also serve as important direct forage sources for large animals, such as Sea Turtles and Manatees (Sea Cows).

Seagrass communities in the Indian River Lagoon begin in the intertidal zone and, because of the lack of consistent water clarity and the fact that they require considerable sunlight for growth, are restricted to above six feet deep, except near the clearer waters of inlets. **Seagrass meadows are food processors**, swarming with crustaceans, snails, worms, mullet, Striped Mojarra, Pinfish and Pigfish, all of which are preferred forage for gamefish such as Tarpon, Redfish, Spotted Seatrout, Snook, jacks, Bluefish, Black Drum, Great Barracuda and Ladyfish. Seagrasses perform ecological functions that are comparable to mangrove forests and salt marsh grasses, including providing shelter, filtering pollutants and binding sediments to help clear the water and prevent coastal erosion. Seagrasses also reduce turbulence and, with their algal epiphytes, absorb excess dissolved nutrients from overly-enriched waters. They contribute immensely to the IRL's stability and productivity. In the absence of seagrasses, the water would become more turbid and sufficient sunlight could not penetrate. Without ample photosynthesis, the process that powers the IRL, the higher levels of the food chain could not exist. **Healthy seagrasses and moderate levels of seaweed epiphytes are the vital foundation of diverse IRL food webs and robust fisheries.**

The Indian River Lagoon's most complex and prolific plant communities are comprised of seven seagrass species— Turtle, Manatee, Widgeon, Shoal, Star, Paddle and Johnson's Seagrasses (see pp. 55–57). Most meadows consist of more than one kind of seagrasses and, in some beds, all seven. Turtle Grass tends to be the longest lived and most resistant to environmental changes. A Turtle Grass community can persist for decades, while patches of diminutive Johnson's Seagrass or Paddle Grass may survive only several months. All seagrasses have roots, stems and leaves that develop from a basal growing region (like lawn grass). Eventually, the ends of the blades die off naturally and are shed as they become colonized by fouling organisms. For this reason, seagrass beds are dynamic, with older portions disintegrating while new leaves crop up continuously.

Because tropical seagrasses grow most abundantly in clear warm water (70° to 90°F), the IRL beds tend to grow rapidly in the summer but may dieback during cold winter conditions (most do persist). Short pulses of cold water are sustainable, but prolonged exposure approaching 45°F can cause sub-

stantial blade losses. Within the Indian River Lagoon, the above tropical seagrasses (with the exception of Shoal Grass) do not survive much farther north than Edgewater, with only Manatee, Shoal, Widgeon and Star Grasses extending north of Sebastian. Even Shoal Grass does not make it beyond the upper two-thirds of the Mosquito Lagoon.

Events that occur far from estuaries can have profound effects on seagrass beds and other marine habitats. For example, the management of Lake Okeechobee sometimes requires releases of freshwater into the St. Lucie Canal. These pulses, coupled with the natural watershed runoff from the St. Lucie River drainage system, can dramatically alter water quality and salinity in the river and, ultimately, the Indian River Lagoon. Restoration of natural, low nutrient, clean, freshwater flow into estuaries can actually improve water quality. Without the freshwater provided by rivers, the lagoon would become too salty for many estuarine species. In addition to freshwater, rivers transport massive quantities of plant debris and dissolved nutrients that provide critically important sustenance for IRL food webs. However, there can be too much of a good thing, and pulses of freshwater at the wrong time can destroy seagrass flats, invertebrate larvae and juvenile fish and shellfish.

Large Schoolmaster Snapper taken on chunked Needlefish.

increasing tourism and recreational opportunities, maintaining property values and stimulating employment. Additionally, the SJRWMD/SFWMD outreach and education program has significantly improved public awareness and support for seagrass restoration as an effective management strategy. **The ongoing SJRWMD/SFWMD seagrass survey and inventory program, monitoring the incredibly complex IRL ecosystem under extremely adverse conditions, is impressive in terms of both the ecological results and the dedication/competence of the field scientists.**

Seagrasses are critically important to all of the inshore and offshore sport fish populations. At some stage in their lives, 70% of the worldwide commercial seafood species depend upon seagrass and other estuarine habitats for their survival. Tropical seagrass beds are exceeded in biological richness only by coral reefs and rain forests. Actually, most of the seagrass bed's community diversity resides in the epiphytic (attached) biota, in particular seaweed epiphytes, but also including many associated invertebrates. The blades (= leaves) of the strap-shaped seagrasses, such as Turtle Grass and Shoal Grass, are literally conveyor belts of various early to late stages of colonization, owing to their production of new leaf growth only at the base. In the healthiest of warm water systems, sediment dwelling rooted forms of green seaweeds, such as native *Caulerpa, Halimeda* and *Penicillus*, are often present interspersed among the grass blades. Look for these deep-rooted green algae as indicators of prime flats fishing habitat in the southern third of the IRL.

In a broad scientific survey covering a range of grass flat systems worldwide, it was concluded that marine seagrasses

Grouper can be taken by trolling or still fishing the ICW where deep rock ledges were uncovered during dredging.

The St. Johns River Water Management District (SJRWMD) and South Florida Water Management District (SFWMD) are two of the organizations charged with managing water quality within the Indian River Lagoon. These organizations actively manage the lagoon to preserve and expand seagrass coverage. Their main agendas for improving water quality are: 1) assisting local governments in controlling and managing storm water runoff; 2) purchasing and restoring fringing wetlands; and 3) working with the Federal Government to design and construct large reservoirs within the St. Lucie River drainage to capture and treat freshwater before releasing it into the estuary. Don't be too critical of the much maligned efforts of the SJRWMD/SFWMD, because they must maintain a careful water balance throughout flood to drought conditions. Given the overabundance of special interest groups (some with diametrically opposite agendas), this is an onerous task indeed! Managing water quality for seagrass health has improved overall conditions within the lagoon, increased habitat quality and quantity and, over the long term, will continue to improve biodiversity within the seagrass meadows. Enriching biodiversity throughout the IRL will make large contributions to the economy of the area by enhancing commercial and sport fisheries stocks,

Turtle Grass beds adjacent to submerged Red Mangrove roots are the habitats of baitfish, such as sardines (Pilchards), and their predators, as in the case of this Great Barracuda and Mangrove Snapper.

View of salt marsh (Cord Grass) mud flat at low tide.

seldom play the predominant direct dietary role in the herbivore link of the food chain. The overwhelming conclusion was that most grazers feed selectively on attached algae, with epiphytic forms supplying at least ten times more organic carbon (food) to grazers than the seagrasses themselves. Because grazing fishes and invertebrates (various tiny to large crustaceans, urchins and snails) feed predominantly on algae, most of the higher-order food chain consumers also depend (indirectly) on algae for their source of organic carbon (food).

In contrast, the seagrasses themselves are seldom directly grazed and ultimately decay (like mangroves and marsh grasses) to form a major component of the sedimentary compost. This organic matter is utilized mostly by bacteria and fungi, a link not prominent in the above algae based chain. Bacteria, fungi and organic debris provide food for mullet and detritus feeders that, in turn, are prey for carnivorous fishes, which ultimately are consumed by humans, shorebirds (such as Herons), diving birds (Ospreys, Brown Pelicans) and Bottle-Nosed Dolphins. Informed sportsmen do not resent these so-called "air wolves" and "sea pigs" or begrudge them their share of the bounty, because their abundances reflect a thriving fishery that is good news to all.

The remarkable assemblage of epiphyte taxa supported by healthy seagrasses includes red algae (such as *Gracilaria and Hypnea*, see p. 58), which dominate in terms of diversity and biomass. Other less desirable epiphytes include the brown alga *Hincksia* in winter (see p. 60), the blue-green alga *Lyngbya* in summer (p. 60) and green algae such as Sea Lettuce *(Entero-morpha)* year-round (p. 59). Astute anglers would do well to learn to recognize these indicator algae; if any of these last three nuisance weeds continually fouls your hooks, you are fishing in less than optimal water quality.

Seagrasses need clean warm water, adequate amounts of sunlight and a balance of sediment bound nutrients. Because all seagrasses can tap the rich nutrients contained in the sediments, excess nutrients in the water surrounding the blades generally favor the competitively superior algae which can be detrimental (by overgrowing the seagrasses). Like all plants, seagrasses and algae use energy from sunlight to convert carbon dioxide, nutrients and water into life sustaining organic compounds (food and oxygen). These carbohydrates and proteins provide nourishment and structure for the plants themselves and to the organisms that consume them.

Monthly blade elongation rates average 2 to 6 inches in Turtle Grass, 10 inches in Manatee Grass and about 12 inches in Shoal Grass. Nearly 10 tons of new leaves per year are produced by a single acre of healthy Turtle Grass. As mentioned, this vast biomass provides food, habitat and nursery areas for the tens of thousands of fish and millions of tiny invertebrates that may reside in a single acre of seagrass. More than 400 species of marine organisms use the vast seagrass beds of the Indian River Lagoon as primary habitat. Owing to their biological and structural roles, as well as their sensitivity to declining water quality, seagrass flats have been recognized by the Water Management Districts as the primary early warning indicators of the overall health of the IRL ecosystem. To put all of this into perspective, seagrasses have both economic and ecological values that the Florida Department of Environmental Protection estimates are worth approximately $20,000 per acre annually. When extrapolated to the entire IRL's seagrass dominated habitats, this figure equates to 1.6 billion dollars per year.

The Indian River Lagoon currently has approximately 80,000 acres of seagrasses, an 18% decline below estimates from aerial photos taken six decades ago. In the long reach from the NASA Causeway to about 10 miles north of Sebastian, a huge highly populated zone served mainly by only septic tank and leach bed sewage treatment (or lack thereof), seagrasses have shown a shocking 70% decline. Interestingly, the dominant Shoal Grass beds in this same area have doubled since 1992—still remaining far below historic abundances. In the central IRL, seagrass coverage has increased markedly from the early 1940's levels, partly correlated with the opening of the Sebastian Inlet in 1948. Another small, but bright, spot is the back country mud-shoal region at the former location of the old Fort Pierce Inlet, which has been colonized in recent years by healthy seagrass stands. In general, seagrass coverage has remained steady or increased in areas retaining natural environmental conditions (Canaveral National Seashore Sanctuary, protected NASA holdings, Merritt Island National Wildlife Refuge), but has declined in those places heavily impacted by development and destruction of wetlands.

SEAGRASS CONSERVATION

The most desirable (healthiest) warm-water grass bed condition, and consequently the most productive sport fish habitat, is indicated by clean seagrass stands such as Turtle Grass, **in association with small amounts of diverse epiphytes and interspersed rooted forms of green algae such as native *Caulerpa*** (see the model below). Healthy grass beds contribute dense biomass and three dimensional structure in clear warm waters where they are anchored in well oxygenated sandy sediments. These are the special haunts of the most knowledgeable and successful flats fishers. Less healthy grass beds (including cold- or salinity-

stressed) are implicated by sparser seagrass stands (particularly Shoal Grass) with increased epiphyte loads of longer filamentous algal forms. Massive overgrowth by long slimy filamentous algal epiphytes (such as *Hincksia* and *Lyngbya*, p. 60), along with inundation by large coarse fleshy algal epiphytes (or even free-lying large masses of unattached fleshy algae), in conjunction with a sparseness of both seagrass and rooted green algal populations, are characteristic of seagrass systems possibly on the verge of collapse. This last condition, if not reversed by epiphyte reductions, leads ultimately to oxygen depletion and to sedimentary barren grounds. The series of grass bed transitional states in the model depicted below is directly related to water quality issues and to the quality of fisheries that each tier in the diagram sustains.

In addition to such stresses as excessive nutrients and reductions in epiphyte grazers, seagrass declines also can result from a number of physical and biological disturbances as in the case of diseases, toxins, violent storms, sedimentation, dredging and salinity/temperature stresses. However, recreational boaters, including fishermen, can also add to seagrass destruction. **Propeller scarring (wheel ditching) by inexperienced boat operators running across shallow grass flats has precipitated the demise of countless acres of habitat.** Generally, if only leaves are chopped, they regrow within weeks. However, when roots and rhizomes are ripped out, the ability to regrow and recover

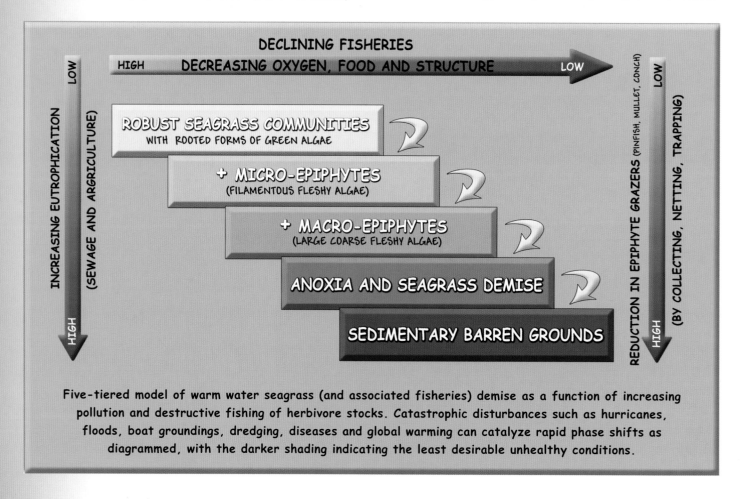

Five-tiered model of warm water seagrass (and associated fisheries) demise as a function of increasing pollution and destructive fishing of herbivore stocks. Catastrophic disturbances such as hurricanes, floods, boat groundings, dredging, diseases and global warming can catalyze rapid phase shifts as diagrammed, with the darker shading indicating the least desirable unhealthy conditions.

Light coatings of algal epiphytes on Turtle Grass, and 'rooted' green seaweeds, such as the *Penicillus* (Mermaid's Shaving Brush, mostly southern IRL) in the center-left, indicate optimally healthy conditions.

light green. Operate your boat at speed only in familiar marked channels to avoid shallow waters. (8) Should you happen to run aground, stop the engine and tilt it all the way up, then pole or walk your boat to deeper water. Never attempt to power (wheel ditch) your way out, which will physically stress your motor's entire lower unit, block coolant passages inside the power head and also quickly destroy the water pump impeller and housing. Furthermore, (9) create environmentally friendly residential landscape designs to minimize water, fertilizer and pesticide use and runoff, and improve septic-tank leaching. (10) Finally, restrict the harvest of algae-eating baitfishes, such as mullet and mature Pinfish, substituting them with plankton feeders like anchovies, sardines and herrings where possible. Each of these choices has an impact on the health of IRL seagrasses. **Virtually everything we do in the Palm, Treasure and Space Coast watersheds influences this keystone resource.**

is lost. **It is not only the relatively small patch damaged that is the issue here, but the newly exposed bare sediments quickly become home to biodestructive burrowing animals**, such as large rays, skates, crabs and Horse Conchs, that continuously expand the barren grounds by their persistent digging/foraging activities. Actual costs of replanting just one acre of damaged seagrass range from $200,000 to $800,000.

The following are 10 recommendations to help boaters and fishermen protect seagrasses: Boaters can prevent grounding impacts by: (1) careful selection of the types of boats purchased and (2) by operating them competently. (3) Additionally, lubricating oils, released underwater in 2-cycle outboard exhausts, coat seagrass, marsh grass and mangrove gas exchange openings. Four stroke units offer the advantages of extremely quiet, more fuel efficient operation, in addition to the highest smoke free emissions ratings. (4) Wear optical quality (not cheap) polarized sunglasses. One of the most important items of navigational safety equipment, polarized sunglasses reduce surface glare, revealing the presence of dark seagrass beds, spoil banks, oyster reefs and animals such as Manatees. (5) Monitor the tides and avoid those seagrass beds that are vulnerable to vessel groundings, even at high tide. (6) Know your travel routes and the location of channel markers. (7) In addition to using the aerial photographs in this guide, obtain a complete set of navigational charts. When running in unfamiliar waters, charts, polarized glasses, high quality aerial photographs and a spotter on the bow enable you to avoid hazards. Seagrass beds are easily discernible in the aerial photographs in this book and are also roughly designated on navigational charts, usually in

Native Great Blue Herons take advantage of exotic Australian Pines for nesting sites on spoil islands.

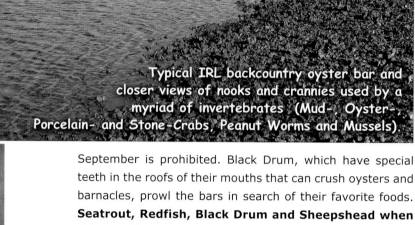

Typical IRL backcountry oyster bar and closer views of nooks and crannies used by a myriad of invertebrates (Mud-, Oyster-, Porcelain- and Stone-Crabs, Peanut Worms and Mussels).

OYSTER REEFS

Oyster reefs form in estuaries where waters are brackish from the intertidal to several feet deep. Within the Indian River Lagoon, oyster reefs are most extensive attached to seawalls, on pilings, adjacent to mangrove and spoil islands and along impoundment dikes. In addition to being commercially valuable, oyster reefs serve a number of important ecological roles by providing hard-bottom attachment sites, removing suspended particles, stabilizing shifting sediments and accelerating current flows.

Indian River Lagoon oyster reefs are built primarily by the Eastern Oyster, which produces planktonic larvae that tend to settle on the shells of other oysters. Unless consumed by predators, continued settlement and subsequent growth of generations of oysters leads to massive reef structures consisting of countless numbers of individuals (see above). As oysters continue to recruit and grow, reefs become more and more complex with many nooks and crannies. These provide a wealth of habitats for a cornucopia of creepy-crawly critters (above), most of them attractive food for gamefish. When a cluster of oysters and barnacles is pried free, a Pandora's Box of tiny worms, crabs, shrimp and other crustaceans scurry in all directions seeking protective cover.

A deadly chumming technique is to remove undesirable oyster fouling colonies from seawalls, break them up over a deep hole or channel next to a grass flat and use some of the oyster meat and associated crab fauna as bait. Remember to check all regulations—harvesting IRL oysters during July through September is prohibited. Black Drum, which have special teeth in the roofs of their mouths that can crush oysters and barnacles, prowl the bars in search of their favorite foods. **Seatrout, Redfish, Black Drum and Sheepshead when driven off the grass flats by winter cold fronts, are to be found in cuts between oyster reefs as well as in nearby deeper channels and holes.**

As discussed earlier, high quality freshwater is a necessity for a healthy estuary. Such valuable shellfish as oysters, crabs and edible shrimp cannot grow without a certain amount of freshwater runoff, which reduces salinity and contains essential nutrients. About 70 percent of Florida's 13 million people live near the coastal zone, making the increasing quantity of runoff pouring into estuaries a major environmental concern. Oysters can improve water quality by straining plankton, suspended organic particles and silt as the water is pumped over their gills. Under optimal conditions, a single oyster may filter as much as 70 gallons of water per day. Extrapolated to the entire IRL, the role of oysters in improving water clarity is immense. Because oysters are sessile and accumulate many toxins and pollutants, they have been used successfully in tissue analyses as site-specific indicators of water quality.

SPOIL ISLANDS AND SHOALS

The Indian River Lagoon portion of the Intracoastal Waterway was deepened by the US Army Corps of Engineers (between 1951 and 1961) to produce a 10–15 feet deep navigational channel. The dredge spoil resulted in 137 spoil islands within the southern counties of the IRL, and another 75 in the Mosquito Lagoon from the subsequent Canaveral and Saturn Barge Canal dredgings. The state owns the majority, while a handful belong to private interests, the US Government or the Florida Inland Navigation District.

The spoil islands have been assigned formal use designations (Conservation, Education and Recreation) determined by their accessibility, richness of native flora and fauna and history

The Indian River Lagoon looking north across the Fort Pierce Inlet. Note the lineup of forested spoil islands in the center of the estuary.

of human usage. Recreational Islands are those where sensitive plants and animals are uncommon and are the only ones available for public use. Most Recreational Islands have long histories of human activity, deep water access points, minimal seagrass flats and contain no threatened species or breeding bird populations. These small to large (to 7.5 acre) wooded islands provide outstanding recreational opportunities for boat campers, beachgoers, picnickers, birders and anglers.

Species diversity and desirable plant cover decrease from south to north on spoil islands. Common native species include mangroves, Cabbage Palm, Gumbo Limbo, Wax Myrtle, Live Oak and Strangler Fig. Australian Pines and Brazilian Pepper are dominant exotic plants that have invaded and outcompeted most of the native species, leading to lower overall plant and animal diversity. However, numerous native bird species do take advantage of this exotic vegetation for nesting sites (p. 11) and certain spoil islands contain some of the most important rookeries in the state.

Many of the shallow submerged dredged-spoil shoals pose a serious navigational hazard to the errant boater who strays to either side of the ICW, but their positive attributes greatly outweigh the negatives. All of these banks and shoals, as well as their underwater habitats, are clearly visible in the aerial photographs found in this book. Many of the same species of fish that feed on grass flats also forage on the dredged aggregate bottoms surrounding spoil shoals and islands. Tailing fish are commonly observed feeding on the shallow sand and gravel bars; whereas, resting Snook, Redfish and Seatrout typically hold in the deeper current channels and holes that are often found on the backsides of spoil islands (opposite the ICW Channel). However, when extensive shallow

bars connect two or more spoil islands, fishing in these backside habitats is much less productive. **Because the spoil banks and islands are so varied in terms of temporal, spatial and seasonal fisheries activities, a dedicated flats angler could devote a career (or a retirement) to mastering this productive portion of the IRL alone.**

Spoil islands are excellent sites for a shore lunch or, in this case, a sunset dinner of barbequed snapper.

13

PRIZED GAMEFISH OF THE INDIAN RIVER LAGOON — THE BIG FOUR!

One focus of this guide book is to allow sportsmen to range farther and wider afield, targeting a broader spectrum of species such as Ladyfish, Black Drum, Lookdown, Bluefish, jacks and Great Barracuda. The recreational pursuit of these sport fish and the more sought-after 'big four', Seatrout, Redfish, Snook and Tarpon, is of huge economic importance. Florida's recreational fisheries were estimated nearly 20 years ago to be worth $5–7 billion, a figure that reflected the booming sport fishing business and all of its spin-off industries.

SPOTTED SEATROUT ('WARY WARRIORS')

Of the 'big four', Spotted Seatrout are the 'Wary Warriors' of the seagrass flats. They range from New York to south Florida and throughout the Gulf of Mexico, preferring water temperatures between 60°–80°F, with spawning occurring at around 75°F. **Because they are unusually sensitive to danger, the most rewarding technique for pursuing Seatrout is classic wade fishing.** Not only does wading lower the angler's profile, it eliminates the noise made by a boat. This enhances the angling experience by adding the tantalizing spot-and-stalk aspect of hunting. For those who prefer to remain in their boats, then stealthy poling or drifting is the most effective method of approach, particularly if the hull design prevents the sound of wave slap.

Seatrout have reflective structures in their eyes that absorb and intensify light in dark murky environments, greatly improving their ability to locate and target prey items. This adaptation as well as large eyes, make them well suited to feeding after dark. **Spotted Seatrout congregate on shallow seagrass meadows to feed from dusk to dawn, requiring anglers to fish for large trout during low light conditions.** Seatrout also hear extremely well and are attracted by subtle noises made by agitated prey, which makes rattle style or splashing top water plugs effective. Aggressive when feeding, Seatrout will readily strike a surface lure, plastic grub, shrimp tipped jig, deer hair fly or any live baitfish.

Unusually hefty specimen of IRL 'gator trout' (Spotted Seatrout). Taken at night at Harbor Branch on light spinning tackle.

Spotted Seatrout also tend to feed (mainly on mullet and Pinfish) when currents are running strong after the initial changing periods of the tides. Spring and early summer are the most productive fishing seasons. Seatrout spawn during April through September, with groups of males setting-up breeding territories in deeper side channels near grass flats. They call (by drumming) to entice roe-laden females throughout the first half of the night. Could fish calling be the next 'hot angling' technique? We would surely like to be able to transmit the recorded distress grunts of a Pigfish into a favorite trout hole! The free floating eggs hatch within several days and then drift for up to a week before the larvae move onto seagrass beds, where they grow rapidly in schools for about 5 years. Males past 5 years old (18 inches) are rare, so all large trout are solitary females.

During the full moon phase, good action can be had night-fishing using flashy/splashy top water baits, such as silver plated poppers and mirrored jerk baits, worked erratically. From winter to late spring, jumbo shrimp, finger mullet, Pinfish and Striped Mojarra are top live

His first 'Copper-Clad Gladiator' (Redfish) — proudly displayed by this Florida sportsman.

bait choices for the famous record-class IRL specimens (called gator trout). Live baits should be drifted or worked slowly. The trick of adding a noisemaking popping bobber to a live bait rig, for attracting Seatrout from afar, has been working for at least 50 years. When fishing for small 1–2 pound schooling trout over grass flats, a soft style grub tipped with a small piece of fresh shrimp is hard to beat. Fly casters take countless Seatrout on deer hair poppers and weedless Clouser Minnows in shrimp patterns. Small Seatrout can usually be found in clean, clear water over rapidly warming shallow flats on sunny fall-winter days.

For bigger fish, look for grassy flats with structural features such as potholes and oyster bars with deep water nearby, where large gator trout station themselves to ambush baitfish. For the wary Seatrout, it is wise to stick with as light a fluorocarbon leader as is practical. For smaller trout, spool lightweight monofilament line and use no leader. Winter Seatrout actively forage just prior to cold fronts. Later during prolonged cold snaps, Seatrout move into deeper waters, such as inlets, man-made canals or the Intracoastal Waterway, that are connected to feeding areas by channels and cuts. Deep running lures or weighted live baits are most productive for gator trout during such severe cold spells. Later on sunny winter days, big Seatrout will move onto shallow northwest flats to bask in the warmer pockets. These 'Wary Warriors' are toothy combatants that frequently take to the air prior to making short drag burning runs. We prefer to carefully release gator trout, since (in our opinion) they are not the best of table fare due to their soft translucent-pink flesh and metallic aftertaste.

REDFISH ('COPPER-CLAD GLADIATORS')

These 'Copper-Clad Gladiators' seem to have been genetically engineered just for the pleasure of the flats angler, particularly fly fishers. Redfish are willing adversaries off every coastal region of mainland Florida. Readily identified by their ventral mouth, eyespots at the base of the tail, reddish coppery hue and rust colored side- and lower-fins, they range from the Gulf of Maine to south Florida and westward in the Gulf of Mexico (where they are most abundant) to northern Mexico. Their optimum temperature range is quite broad, 50°–80°F. Redfish eagerly take live, cut and artificial baits, whether presented on the bottom, at mid-depths or on the surface, and can be landed using spinning, casting or fly rod techniques. Their only shortcoming is that they refuse to jump, but sizable Redfish do make powerful runs and pull with a bulldog tenacity that can cramp your hands, arms, shoulders and back. Last but not least, if you are hungry for the best of 'piscatorial cuisine', Redfish filets are firm and delicious, whether fried, baked, broiled, grilled or blackened.

You don't have to be much of an old-timer to remember when Redfish nearly disappeared in the late 1980's, due to the popularization of a blackened Redfish recipe and the concomitant nationwide craving for this spicy dish. However, because fisheries managers rapidly instituted fishing moratoriums, leading to less-stringent regulations (slot limits, restricted seasons and a one fish daily bag limit), this important fishery has been resurrected. On a lagoon wide basis, Redfish now rank among the most consistent of inshore catches. The

Completed 'Billy-the-Crab' will slowly sink with upraised claws and be fairly weedless. The Green Clinging Crab is an herbivorous crab that is obscure to fly anglers, but well known to Permit, Bonefish, all drums, including Redfish, and other crab eaters.

Mosquito Lagoon systems. There, many Redfish spawn and remain in the estuary all their lives, because of higher salinities and remote access to inlets, where they reach prodigious sizes. Redfish live to at least 53 years old, the age of the 94 pound all-tackle record.

Along with the popularity of Bonefish, Permit and Tarpon, Redfish have catalyzed runaway sales of flats skiffs, costly high-tech vessels that provide access to waters less than eight inches deep. Redfish, however, show no 'boat snobbery' and anglers with any shallow draft craft can catch them. **Wading from highway access points or hiking-in on impound-ment dikes is particularly effective for accessing schooling Redfish.** Some fishing fanatics have even been known to 'road hunt' them by glassing from cars along parallel roadways. Low water forces Redfish off the shallower flats, concentrating their numbers and also making their wakes ('worried water') more visible from nearby roads. Skinny water skiffs are great, but once fish are sighted, wade fishing is more productive and exciting.

near loss of this treasured fishery, followed by its rejuvenation, has given thoughtful anglers a new attitude toward the 'Copper-Clad Gladiator'. Sportsman are now more altruistic and can be satisfied with a four pounder, instead of filling the freezer with juveniles or large 'breeder' specimens. Secondly, responsible anglers who land undersized fish now meticulously release them with considerable care, making sure that they survive to be enjoyed again.

Upon attaining a length of about 30 inches (4-5 years), Redfish leave the Indian River Lagoon on a one-way journey to join spawning populations in nearshore waters off inlets. They then move to offshore federal waters (to 200 feet deep) where they are totally protected. During breeding, the males chase and bump the females while drumming, a sound they produce by rubbing a muscle against their inflated swim bladders. Spawning takes place from August to November and the eggs hatch within one day. The larvae are then carried into the IRL via the inlets by tidal flood currents. The juveniles and young adults prefer shallow marsh/mud areas and sparse seagrass beds. They tolerate low salinity water better as juveniles, possibly even requiring freshwater at this stage; whereas, mature Redfish seek higher salinities.

Redfish below breeding size remain inshore patrolling oyster bars, surge channels, tidal creeks, hard-bottoms and grass flats. They grow rapidly and the 18–27 inch slot-limit size is exceeded in less than one year's growth, minimizing each fish's exposure to being 'released in hot cooking oil'. An exception to offshore migration occurs in the northernmost Indian River, Banana River and

Redfish characteristically meander along slowly, particularly where salt marshes meet mud flats, stopping occasionally to root out a buried crab with their tails prominently in view. During slicked-off conditions, tailing Reds can be seen from hundreds of feet away by their square reddish tails with blue margins. Redfish that are feeding intensively expose the entire tail, including the eyespot at the base. Hasten toward these fish quietly, approaching no nearer than the length of your most comfortable casting distance. When wading, sneak in low to reduce your profile. It has been said that "a mature Redfish has been hooked so many times that it is more familiar with terminal tackle than the average fisherman".

Once a Redfish is on, the others in the school typically become excited and lose much of their natural caution, darting around the hooked fish. If a second angler is able to quickly drag a bait into these frenzied fish, a double hookup is likely. Fly fishers use this technique to good advantage. Since spin casters can throw a weighted lure much farther than most fly anglers can present a fly, a partner using spinning tackle and a gold spoon (usually) hooks the first fish and draws the school closer to the boat. The fly rodder then casts a chartreuse streamer or gold

Tying the 'Billy-the-Crab' fly first involves puffing a pinch of olive-green bucktail.

spoon-fly into their midst and the resulting pandemonium is long remembered. We have developed our own deadly saltwater fly that imitates the ubiquitous Green Clinging Crab *(Mithrax sculptus)*. Step-by-step photographs on tying the 'Billy-the-Crab' are on pp. 16–17. **Any fish that eats small crabs (Permit, Bonefish, Redfish etc.), particularly those that are weary of being pounded by streamers and Clousers, simply cannot refuse this pattern.**

Bull Redfish, unlike the other 'big four', don't panic when first hooked, perhaps hoping that "this is not really happening to me", but as soon as they become aware of the eminent danger, they square their

The 'Fighting Robalo'—a nice Common Snook taken on light spinning tackle.

shoulders and accelerate under a full-head-of-steam. As their bullish efforts subside they begin side rolling, but upon spotting the boat they usually get a second wind and go into a head shaking mode characteristic of the younger fish. There is also a stereotypical behavior of just-released Reds, which usually dive to the bottom until they catch their breath. They then dart straight away, almost always in the direction of the school, giving the astute angler a clue for follow-up catches.

With the onset of colder weather in the fall, non-breeding Redfish (like Snook) move into tidal creeks, deep passes and coastal rivers. Once they enter tannin stained waters, their subtle tints of rose-pink deepen to glistening coppery bronze, a fiery sheen that is spectacular even to the most indifferent of non-fishing spouses.

COMMON SNOOK ('FIGHTING ROBALO')

The 'Fighting Robalo' of the mangrove fringe is anything but common! This awesome high jumping battler is the fish Largemouth Bass anglers wish they could have in their rivers and lakes. More than one member of the glitter boat fraternity, upon catching that first Snook, has become addicted to saltwater angling for life. The Fighting Robalo is a fish that will use any tactic to win, even going so far as to pull-a-knife! This brings

us to the one drawback to this brawler—the razor-sharp blades on the cheek plates. These pointed blades will readily slice the heaviest nylon monofilament lines, necessitating short fluorocarbon leaders of at least 30–50 pound-test (conspicuous wire leaders just won't cut it—no pun intended).

Widely known as Robalo, the Common Snook is identified by its thin black lateral line (from the top of the gill cover through the tail), clean cut streamlined body, slightly concave forehead and large mouth with an upturned projecting lower jaw. The broad shouldered upper body is dark yellowish to greenish brown in color with a silver-white belly and yellow ventral fins and tail. The 'Fighting Robalo' is bound to waters off land masses that have substantial freshwater rivers. It normally ranges from about Cape Canaveral to Rio de Janeiro, Brazil, including the Greater Antilles, southern Gulf of Mexico and the Caribbean coasts of Central and South America—with the center of abundance being our own Indian River Lagoon. Snook are temperature tolerant, but sensitive to cold, with their limits not extending to waters beyond the 50°F isotherms.

Snook populations have declined over the last 50 years due to both habitat destruction and overharvesting; in the IRL, habitat loss (urbanization, impoundments) and water quality degradation (excess nutrients) have had the greatest effects

Final stages involve trimming the body and adding olive-green feather claws and legs, as well as melted monofilament stalked eyes, using a light coating of quick setting clear epoxy to attach and strengthen the appendages.

17

by far. Consequently, Snook now have been granted gamefish status and are regulated by the requirement for a special stamp, restricted seasons, size and daily limits.

Mature Snook do not travel great distances. However, they leave their overwintering locations in upper-estuarine low-salinity waters and migrate toward the inlet spawning grounds in early spring, where they remain for the duration of the summer. The wintering grounds provide sanctuary, during cold induced periods of lethargic vulnerability, from such major predators as sharks, Bottle-Nosed Dolphins, Barracudas and humans. All Snook are ambush predators and will not pursue prey for great distances. However, they are efficient carnivores, feeding primarily on fish and crustaceans, mostly targeting mullet, anchovies, herring, sardines, Pinfish, Pigfish, crabs and shrimp. **It is most important for anglers to know that Snook (as in Spotted Seatrout) mainly feed during low light periods, with peak activities occurring a couple of hours prior to and slightly after sunrise as well as just before and several hours after sunset.** Feeding activity (also as in Seatrout) increases as a function of accelerated water flow following the peak flood- and ebb-tide stages.

There are three other smaller less abundant Snook species (Swordspine, Tarpon and Fat Snook, pp. 26–27) that co-occur in Florida, although these mostly live far up in the southernmost coastal rivers and estuaries. A challenge for any light tackle angler would be a 'Snook Slam' (all four species) or, to kick it up a couple of notches, a 'Snook Super Slam' (all on fly rod the same day!). The latter angling achievement is, to our knowledge, yet to be documented.

Common Snook occur throughout the IRL, where their abundances center on mangrove fringes, seagrass flats and channels within 15 miles of inlets. Snook live for over 20 years and can exceed 55 inches in length, with the record all-tackle Snook, caught in Costa Rica, weighing 53 pounds and 10 ounces. Like Spotted Seatrout and Tarpon, female specimens are typically larger than males of the same age class. In marked contrast, however, Snook undergo a sexual transition from males to females between the ages of 1 to 7 years, so all lunker Snook are transformed females (would you believe hermaphrodites?). Although adult Snook may utilize freshwater habitats, they are unable to spawn in freshwater. Snook species in the IRL congregate at the mouths of coastal rivers and inlets to spawn during the late afternoon and early evening, irrespective of tidal stages or lunar periods, over the course of the May through September breeding season. Schools of mature Snook, numbering in the hundreds, consistently return to the same spawning locations year after year. After the eggs hatch, the larvae drift for several days before the juveniles become capable of seeking out freshwater tributaries, grassy marshes and mangrove fringes.

The wide salinity tolerance of Snook accommodates various habitat choices as they travel through freshwater, brackish and marine regions. Habitat features sought out by Snook include good water quality, moderate currents, overhanging tree limbs, mangrove prop roots and structures such as docks, posts, rocks and steep dropoffs. However, the largest specimens are to be found under the many causeway bridges and in the inlets. Snook can be caught by trolling the bridge pilings and the edges of dropoffs near overhanging mangrove limbs when the sun is low on the horizon. For casting to Snook, use the same flies, jigs, jerk baits and live baits as discussed earlier for Seatrout. Remember, Snook are ambush predators and will not chase a lure very far; however, be careful not to 'bean' them when targeting spots beneath docks and overhangs. Robalo usually remain non-migratory as adults, except for the breeding congregations mentioned above. Spot, Striped Mojarra, Striped and Silver Mullet, Sheepshead, Ladyfish and Tarpon are all closely associated with the 'Fighting Robalo'.

These two longtime fishing buddies collaborated on this trophy-sized (12 pound) Bonefish. Bones are taken on isolated flats in the southern IRL during late summer.

TARPON ('SILVER KINGS')

Tarpon are large, deep bodied fish commonly found in coastal and inshore waterways. If Redfish are the 'Copper-Clad Gladiators', then Tarpon are the 'Silver Kings' of the shallows, having had 125 million years to perfect their blend of form and function. They have cruised tropical seas since the era when dinosaurs ruled the planet. The Tarpon has retained a unique rudimentary lung (blood enriched convoluted air bladder connected to the throat by a specialized tube), that allows it to take an occasional gulp of air while rolling at the surface and, hence, thrive in oxygen depleted waters. Tarpon range in the Western Atlantic from Nova Scotia to Brazil, including Bermuda, the Caribbean, the Gulf of Mexico and along the coast of western Africa, attaining a length of at least 8 feet and a weight of 280 pounds. Tarpon are sexually separate, with females growing larger than males. One female just under 7 feet long was aged at approximately 55 years.

Adult Tarpon make extensive roundtrip spawning migrations from inshore waters to remote blue water spawning grounds 125 miles offshore in the Gulf of Mexico, or closer off the Florida Keys, from late July through August. The adults spend the winter months well offshore and move into the IRL in May through July strictly to feed, mostly on crabs, mullet and Pinfish. This is the time that Tarpon return en masse to the IRL, and anglers casting flies, jerk baits, plugs and live bait will challenge behemoths to 150 pounds.

Like other species that spawn in open oceanic waters, female Tarpon release enormous numbers of eggs, often in excess of 15 million. At least 10 years are required for Tarpon to become sexually mature. Their eel-like larvae feed on microscopic plankton as they drift shoreward for 30–40 days. After 3–4 months of rapid larval growth, these toothy creatures take on the unmistakable form of baby Tarpon, complete with mirrored scales and oversized eyes. These juveniles navigate toward inland estuaries during June and July, running a gauntlet of carnivores, to seek out waters so diluted and stagnant that neither their competitors nor their predators can follow. Within one year, they are over a foot long and can avoid most carnivores, notwithstanding birds and dolphins.

Everything about the 'Silver King' is large scale (no pun intended). More than a few fortunate anglers, quietly fishing alone in calm remote backwaters, have experienced passing schools of giant Tarpon shimmering like huge silver ghosts, all of them half as long as a skiff, with belligerent lower jaws protruding from their prehistoric heads. On such rare occasions, even the most cool headed angler experiences a suffocating adrenaline rush that only repeated encounters can calm to some semblance of casting competence. The red rimmed threatening eyes suggest the Tarpon's scientific name *Megalops* (meaning big eye) and up close, no matter what the viewing angle, you become convinced that this intimidating fish is trying to freeze you in its stare.

Baby Tarpon taken with fly tackle make for adrenaline pumping action.

Nevertheless, anglers do bring Tarpon to hand throughout every waterway and remote byway of the Indian River Lagoon. There is no other place where Tarpon are as revered as they are in Florida, where top Tarpon anglers are unequalled in professionalism. No other inshore fish can compare to Tarpon, which average 65 pounds each. A giant Tarpon is almost never hooked and landed by accident and will always win the majority of its encounters with light tackle sportsmen. **The 'Silver King' absolutely freaks-out when first hooked, performing a signature series of moves.** It initially erupts from the water three or more times in rapid-fire leaps that are wild explosions of riveting electricity, a magnificent silver rocket launching itself high out of its aquatic realm with reckless abandon. If Tarpon were to run straight away instead of expending energy on towering gill rattling acrobatics, landing one on other than very heavy tackle would be highly unlikely. The experienced angler will bow down to a jumping Tarpon; not in deference, but to take tension off the overstressed line. After performing this patented opening gambit of aerial maneuvers, each fish rips off a fair amount of line and then launches itself again. By that time, the seasoned sportsman has had time to recover a modicum of composure, get loose line onto the reel and prepare for long, drag-screaming, fish-chasing runs and an exhausting battle of wills, interspersed with unrelenting aerial displays.

Techniques for catching 'Silver Kings' vary widely, but locating the fish in calm water is straightforward. The fish roll at the surface periodically, taking an obligatory swallow of air, which provides additional oxygen essential for their survival. Anglers shut down the outboard, pole into calm bays where Tarpon are likely to be found and watch and listen for any telltale activity. Tarpon eat almost anything, but tend to focus on upper water column fishes such as menhaden, sardines, anchovies, herring, mullet, Snook and Pinfish, but also consume prodigious quantities of shrimp and crabs. Heavy tackle, 4 feet of 60–80 pound-test fluorocarbon leader, a #5/0 circle hook, live or dead baits under bobbers and a quick release anchor line (rigged with a large ball float) is the most effective big fish setup in deeper channels and inlets. Many guides prefer this system since it allows novice clients to experience the unbridled energy of the 'Silver King'.

Another shortcut technique used by some guides is to suspend chum cages at the surface and watch for rolling fish in the oily slick. When Tarpon appear, the customer drifts a live bait toward them. Tackle usually is very heavy so that clients can have a fighting chance. Feeding Tarpon willingly strike bucktail jigs; jerk baits and crank baits, as well as the array of soft plastic lures used by freshwater bass fishermen. With skill and perseverance, sportsmen in small boats can land Tarpon using medium to heavy spinning tackle. **It is important for small boat anglers to plan ahead on how to react quickly to a hookup, especially if a 'mega-*Megalops*' decides to run for distant waters or, worse, jumps right into the boat.**

The most challenging and sporting technique, both for thrills and frustration, is spot-and-stalk fishing for large Tarpon using fly tackle, usually rigged with a brown Tarpon-streamer (white or chartreuse in stained waters), on shallow grass flats. This stealthy form of the sport is becoming extremely popular as it adds the most suspenseful aspects of hunting/stalking.

The 'Silver King' is without doubt the most prestigious of inshore gamefish due to its outrageous acrobatics, tremendous strength and blazing speed. Fortunately, it has zero value as a food fish. Therefore, killing a Tarpon is seldom justified and destroys a creature that took nearly three decades to produce. Since 1989,

Palometa are uncommon, but feisty on fly tackle.

implementation of the 'tag system' in the Tarpon fishery has required anglers to pre-purchase a $50 tag to kill a Tarpon. This process has all but eliminated catch-and-kill fishing for this species. Deaths are minimal when fish hooked in the jaw are quickly brought to the side of the boat and set free. If a wall trophy is a must, get a quick snapshot and estimate length and girth to order a long lasting lightweight replica that is far more attractive and accurate than a painted skin mount of a once living fish. Release the 'Silver King' with care, watch it return to nature undamaged and take justifiable pride in a triumphant personal accomplishment.

FISHERIES CONSERVATION

As conservation ethics grow stronger among saltwater sportsman, catch-and-release has become increasingly important. Anglers are well aware of the results of overfishing and are using sophisticated techniques to reduce negative impacts. **The majority of angling outings in the Indian River Lagoon result in most of the fish landed being set free.** Regulated species, such as Redfish, Seatrout and Snook, must be released if they are outside their slot limits. Many professional guides and sportsmen go afield with the intention of releasing every animal landed. The Tarpon fishery is an example of such a highly successful no-kill management program.

Most of the following techniques are recommended by the Florida Fish and Wildlife Conservation Commission (FWC) to increase the survival of released fish: (1) Select tackle that will avoid the need to play the fish to exhaustion, which puts the fish at risk due to lactic acid buildup or predation. **Experienced anglers minimize battles and spend considerable time reviving fish by facing them into the current until the fish is ready to swim away** (a BogaGrip lip clamp is good for this). Fish should never be tossed or dropped onto their sides. (2) **Use barbless hooks, or flatten the barb, as one of the most important techniques** to increase hookups, minimize internal damage and make release quicker. Fisheries regulations prohibit the use of treble hooks with either dead or live natural baits. With natural baits, use barbless circle hooks to reduce gut hooking, increase your hookup ratio and facilitate release. (3)

Between a rock and a hard place — Crevalle Jacks chopping sardines against the shore — and Snowy Egrets in a coordinated attack by land.

Fishing with artificial lures reduces the likelihood of gut hooking fish, whereas using live baits increases that risk. **It is most effective to use circle hooks with live bait and to take up the line instantly upon detecting a bite.** The survival rate of gut hooked fish increases if the line is cut close to the hook; avoid lifting gut hooked fish by the leader to minimize internal damage. (4) Keeping fish in the water until release is desirable; but not always practical. Removing an exhausted fish from the water is like submerging the head of a long distance runner at the finish line. A quick release landing device (such as a BogaGrip) clamps even the toothiest fish's lower jaw and is the way that most professional anglers prefer to control and handle their catches. If fish must be lifted without benefit of a BogaGrip, they should be gently cradled under the belly using wet hands. Dry hands, towels, gloves and string-mesh landing nets remove much of the protective coating, increasing the risk of fungal infections. **Never grasp fish with contact to the gill rakers or by the eyes.** In general, handle catches as little as possible and free them quickly. Some species can be calmed during release handling by turning them onto their backs. To quickly remove the hook, use high quality needle-nose pliers (such as the Donnmar brand) or a quality dehooker. Keep these tools in a consistent, accessible location so fish can be dealt with quickly. (5) Large gamefish such as sharks and Tarpon should be brought alongside as quickly as possible. **Do not boat large fish—they can be dangerous to both themselves and the fisherman.** Fish that are in good condition should be set free immediately by removing the hook or cutting the leader close to the hook. Artificial lures with flattened barbs will facilitate release, and circle hooks (with natural baits) will reduce gut hooking. If the fish is exhausted, revive it in the shade, making sure the head is totally submerged and moving it slowly (not herky-jerky) back and forth; or better still, hold it lightly facing into the current.

(6) While there is nothing wrong with harvesting a full legal limit, day after day that quantity leads to unnecessary depletion of gamefish stocks. **The future for continued availability of quality gamefish rests on all responsible sportsman limiting kills, rather than killing limits.** Many guides and sportsman now free all gamefish regardless of size, with the conviction that their destiny should be to live to fight again.

Become the Consummate All-Around Angler: Fortunately, sport fishing has come of age, where skilled sportsmen are broadening their horizons and all-around angling skills. Seasoned anglers diversify by targeting many of the more readily harvestable species, including such battlers as Crevalle Jack, Bluefish, mackerel and bottom feeders such as snapper, grouper, Black Drum, Sheepshead, Florida Pompano and flounder for smoked fish recipes and other table fare. The promotion of angling diversity is the point behind the FWC Grand Slam Certificates. By emphasizing the challenge and achievement of catching three different species of gamefish (in the same day), the intent is to recognize broad based angling skills rather than targeting any single species. **By becoming diverse and adaptive sportsmen, anglers provide the 'big four' gamefish a critically needed reprieve.**

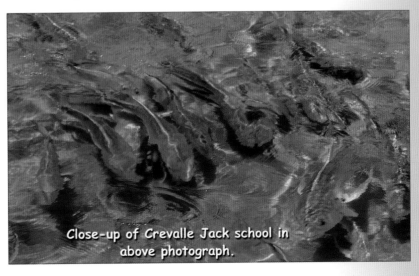

Close-up of Crevalle Jack school in above photograph.

COMMON GAMEFISH AND BAITFISH OF THE INDIAN RIVER LAGOON

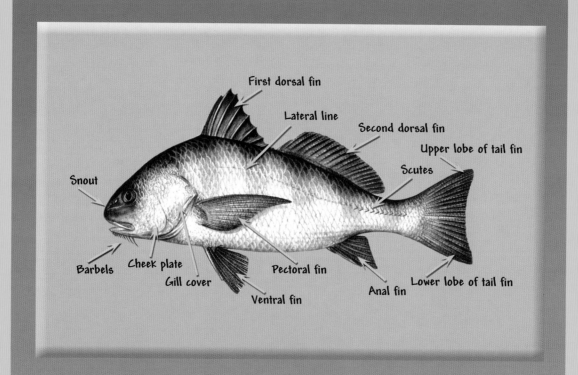

First dorsal fin

Lateral line

Second dorsal fin

Upper lobe of tail fin

Snout

Scutes

Barbels

Cheek plate

Gill cover

Pectoral fin

Ventral fin

Anal fin

Lower lobe of tail fin

ATLANTIC SHARPNOSE SHARK

Rhizoprionodon terraenovae, FAMILY CARCHARHINIDAE (REQUIEM SHARKS)

Description: *Color* brown, olive-gray to gray; pale below; pectoral fin with white trailing edge; dorsal and tail fins with black edge; occasionally with light spots on sides; fin coloration more distinct in juveniles. *Body* small, streamlined; snout long, slightly flattened, pointed; mouth with furrows at corners; second dorsal fin origin over middle of anal fin; upper lobe of tail much larger than lower lobe.

Size: Maximum length 3.6 ft.; maximum weight 16 lb.

Diet: Small fish, shrimp, crabs, worms and molluscs; scavenger.

Utilization: Gamefish; marketed fresh or salted.

Note: Medium casting or spinning tackle. Use cut mullet and croakers on bottom or cut bait in chum slick; rig with 15-20 lb. test line, 3 feet of wire leader, Sampo swivel and relatively large circle hook (5/0). Jumps and spins when hooked. Never tail-land any shark; they are very flexible (cartilaginous) and can easily twist around to bite your hand, or worse!

BLACKNOSE SHARK

Carcharhinus acronotus, FAMILY CARCHARHINIDAE (REQUIEM SHARKS)

Description: *Color* pale olive-gray; lighter to whitish below; dusky to black smudge at snout tip, fades with age. *Body* long, sleek; first dorsal fin begins above back corner of pectoral fin; upper lobe of tail much larger than lower lobe.

Size: Maximum length 6.5 ft.; maximum weight 41.7 lb.

Diet: Small fish, especially Pinfish; scavenger.

Utilization: Gamefish; prepared salted and dried.

Note: Use cut bait or shrimp in chum slick on bottom with medium tackle; rig with 4 feet of wire leader and circle hook.

TOP VIEW

BONNET-HEAD

Sphyrna tiburo, FAMILY SPHYRNIDAE (HAMMERHEADS, SCOOPHEADS)

Description: *Color* gray to gray-brown; darker above; lighter below; rarely with small dark spots on sides. *Body* with distinctive broadly widened, spade-shaped or shovel-like head with eyes located at far ends of side lobes (see above inset); front of head semicircular in outline; tail with large upper lobe.

Size: Maximum length 5 ft.; maximum weight 28.8 lb. [IRL commonly 3–4 ft. long]

Diet: Crustaceans (particularly blue crabs), also bivalves, octopus and small fish; scavenger.

Utilization: Commercial (fishmeal); gamefish.

Note: Indicator of good flats fishing habitat; great sport on light tackle and fly gear. Sight cast shrimp or cut bait; rig with 2-3 feet of wire leader and circle hook.

BULL SHARK

Carcharhinus leucas, FAMILY CARCHARHINIDAE (REQUIEM SHARKS)

Description: *Color* gray to brown; darker above; lighter below; fin tips dark, fading with age. *Body* massive; snout short, broad, blunt; eyes small; upper teeth triangular, saw-edged; first dorsal fin broad, triangular, 3 times higher than second dorsal fin.

Size: Maximum length 11.5 ft.; maximum weight 698 lb.; maximum age 32 years. [Florida records: conventional 517 lb.; fly fishing 389 lb. 4 oz.]

Diet: Fish, other sharks, rays, mud shrimp, crabs, squid, sea snails, sea urchins and sea turtles; scavenger.

Utilization: Commercial; aquarium; gamefish; marketed fresh, frozen or smoked; fins for soup; hide for leather; liver for oil; carcass for fishmeal.

Note: Rugged fighter. Use cut bait (especially cut Barracuda); heavy tackle, rig with 4 feet of wire leader and circle hook; use chum with artificials, large flies best.

LEMON SHARK

Negaprion brevirostris

FAMILY CARCHARHINIDAE (REQUIEM SHARKS)

Description: *Color* brown to gray; darker above; lighter with yellow tones below. *Body* large; eyes small; first dorsal fin large, triangular, not much larger than second dorsal fin.

Size: Maximum length 11.1 ft.; maximum weight 405 lb. [Florida records: conventional 396 lb.; fly fishing 288 lb. 8 oz.]

Diet: Primarily fish, also takes crustaceans and molluscs.

Utilization: Commercial; gamefish; marketed fresh, salted or frozen; hides for leather; fins for soup; liver for oil; carcass for fishmeal.

Note: Great sport on light tackle and fly gear. Sight cast live or cut bait; will occasionally take artificials; rig with 2-3 feet of wire leader and circle hook.

SOUTHERN STINGRAY

Dasyatis americana, FAMILY DASYATIDAE (STINGRAYS)

Description: *Color* uniformly dark brown to gray (or olive green) above, grayer when young; white below, often with gray or brown edging. *Body* disk-like; outer corners sharp; back with irregular row of short spines; well-developed saw-toothed barb at base of tail capable of inflicting painful laceration.

Size: Maximum length 6.6 ft.; maximum weight 298.9 lb.

Diet: Invertebrates (clams) and small fish; scavenger.

Utilization: Commercial; gamefish, highly-cartilaginous flesh.

Note: Good indicator of prime fishing flats, often accompanied by Permit and Bonefish. Use light tackle; sight cast cut bait, squid chunks or shrimp.

LADYFISH

Elops saurus, FAMILY ELOPIDAE (TENPOUNDERS)

Description: *Color* silver; bluish above; pale yellow below; fins dusky with yellow tinge. *Body* long, slender; head small, pointed; tail large, deeply forked; scales small.

Size: Maximum length 39.4 inches; maximum weight 22.3 lb. [Florida records: conventional 6 lb.; fly fishing 5 lb. 6 oz.]

Diet: Crustaceans and small fish; often seen in large schools pursuing prey near surface.

Utilization: Minor commercial; gamefish; baitfish; marketed fresh, salted or frozen; considered a second-rate food fish due to many bones and mushy flesh.

Note: Willingly takes Tarpon lures; great jumper; fun action schooling fish. Use light tackle with live and cut baits, small jigs, plugs or spoons; rig with light nylon coated wire leader.

TARPON

Megalops atlanticus, FAMILY MEGALOPIDAE (TARPONS)

Description: *Color* generally silver, occasionally golden brown in estuaries; dark blue to green above; lighter below. *Body* large, elongated, moderately compressed; scales huge; mouth large, upturned; lower jaw projecting beyond upper jaw; swim bladder can be filled directly with air, enabling species to live in oxygen-poor waters; last ray of dorsal fin long, slender, filament-like; tail deeply forked.

Size: Maximum length 8.2 ft.; maximum weight 283 lb.; maximum age 55 years. [Florida records: conventional 243 lb.; fly fishing 202 lb. 8 oz.]

Diet: Fish (mainly those forming schools such as mullet, sardines, herring, anchovies and Pinfish), shrimp and crabs.

Utilization: Banned commercial; aquarium; gamefish; not good food fish because of bony flesh and poor taste.

Note: One of the most sought after and challenging of sport fish, famous for its spectacular jumps, strength and stamina. Its hard bony jaws make it difficult to hook and a challenge for skilled anglers. In Florida waters, Tarpon are protected under the 1 fish, $50 tag program, see details in the 'Silver King' section (p. 19).

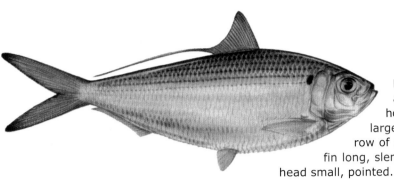

ATLANTIC THREAD HERRING (GREENIE)

Opisthonema oglinum, FAMILY CLUPEIDAE (HERRINGS, SHADS)

Description: *Color* silver; darker blue, gray to greenish above; silver-white below; occasionally with 6-7 horizontal dark streaks on back; dark spot above gill cover, larger dark spot behind gill cover, frequently followed by row of smaller dark spots. *Body* with last ray of single dorsal fin long, slender, filament-like; lower profile (belly) deeply curved; head small, pointed.

Size: Maximum length 16 inches; maximum weight 14 oz.

Diet: Suspended microscopic crustaceans; secondarily small fish, crabs and mysid shrimp.

Utilization: Commercial; mainly baitfish; marketed fresh, frozen or salted; also used for fishmeal, good fresh bait.

Note: Caught with a Sabiki rig (a spread of 6 tiny jigs) or cast net.

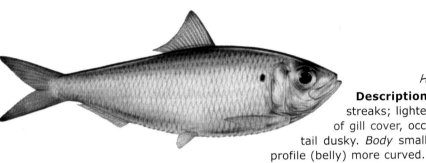

SCALED SARDINE (PILCHARD)

Harengula jaguana, FAMILY CLUPEIDAE (HERRINGS, SHADS)

Description: *Color* silver; back with several faint dark streaks; lighter below; single small dark spot at upper edge of gill cover, occasionally another on shoulder; dorsal fin and tail dusky. *Body* small, compressed; upper profile flattened; lower profile (belly) more curved.

Size: Maximum length 8.3 inches; maximum weight 1 lb.

Diet: Zooplankton (suspended microscopic animals).

Utilization: Minor commercial; delicate baitfish; marketed fresh or canned.

Note: Caught with Sabiki rig (a spread of 6 tiny jigs) or cast net.

SPANISH SARDINE

Sardinella aurita, FAMILY CLUPEIDAE (HERRINGS, SHADS)

Description: *Color* silver to brass; blue-gray, dark blue to greenish above; lateral line faint, gold; pale golden spot behind gill opening; black spot at posterior border of gill cover. *Body* slender, somewhat cylindrical or slightly compressed; scutes along belly obvious; ventral fin with 8 rays.

Size: Maximum length 12.2 inches; maximum weight 8 oz.

Diet: Zooplankton, especially copepods.

Utilization: Highly commercial; marketed fresh or canned; used mostly for bait.

Note: Caught with Sabiki rig or cast net, easily chummed.

GULF MENHADEN (SHAD, POGIE)

Brevoortia patronus, FAMILY CLUPEIDAE (HERRINGS, SHADS)

Description: *Color* silver to brass-green; blue-gray to blue-brown above; lighter below; black spot behind gill, often followed by series of spots. *Body* compressed, deep; head large; scutes along belly; lower jaw fits into middle notch of upper jaw.

Size: Maximum length 13.8 inches.

Diet: Filters phytoplankton (suspended microscopic plants); also a bottom feeder.

Utilization: Highly commercial; marketed fresh, salted or canned; used for fish oil and fish meal; baitfish.

Note: Caught with Sabiki rig or cast net.

YELLOWFIN MENHADEN

Brevoortia smithi, FAMILY CLUPEIDAE (HERRINGS, SHADS)

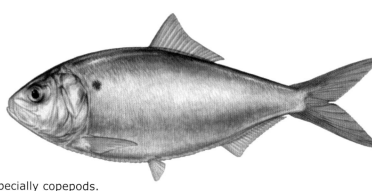

Description: *Color* silver; greenish or bluish above; fins golden yellow; black spot behind gill opening. *Body* compressed, deep; scutes along belly; upper jaw with center notch; scales small, those on back smaller than those on sides.

Size: Maximum length 13 inches.

Diet: Zooplankton (suspended microscopic animals), especially copepods.

Utilization: Minor commercial; baitfish.

Note: Caught with Sabiki rig (6 tiny jigs) or cast net.

BALLYHOO

Hemiramphus brasiliensis

FAMILY HEMIRAMPHIDAE (HALFBEAKS)

Description: *Color* silver; blue, green or blue-green metallic luster on back; tip of lower jaw and upper lobe of tail orange-red. *Body* slender; lower jaw much elongated; pectoral (side) fins short; lower lobe of tail longer than upper lobe.

Size: Maximum length 21.6 inches; maximum weight 1 lb.

Diet: Seagrasses (mostly drift Manatee Grass, p. 55) and small fish.

Utilization: Minor commercial; major baitfish.

Note: Used as rigged trolling bait for offshore billfish, also in IRL as cut bait. Fish immediately off stern with surface chum bag, when Ballyhoo appear use ultralight line and small gold hook (#10) tipped with shrimp. Also taken by cast net.

FAT SNOOK

Centropomus parallelus, FAMILY CENTROPOMIDAE (SNOOKS)

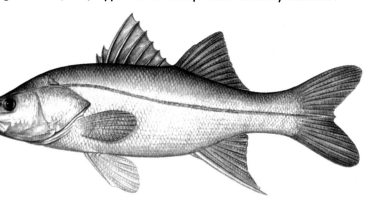

Description: *Color* silver; yellow-brown to green-brown above; lighter silver-white below; lateral line thin, black, extending from top of gill cover through tail; ventral fin yellow. *Body* deep; forehead slightly depressed, sloping; lower jaw protruding; mouth large; scales smaller than Common Snook; dorsal fins high with little or no space between first and second.

Size: Maximum length 28.3 inches; maximum weight 11 lb.

Diet: Fish and crustaceans (shrimp and crabs).

Utilization: Gamefish (only snook besides the Common Snook large enough for legal harvest); good food fish.

Note: Hard strikers and good fighters despite small size. Fish mangrove margins and channels. Casting or trolling with medium to light action spinning and casting gear or 5–8 weight fly tackle. Use small jigs, surface and swimming plugs, streamer flies, popping bugs or live bait (shrimp or small baitfish).

COMMON SNOOK (ROBALO)

Centropomus undecimalis, FAMILY CENTROPOMIDAE (SNOOKS)

Description: *Color* silver; dark yellow to green-brown above; lighter silver-white below; lateral line thin, black, extending from top of gill cover through tail; ventral fin yellow. *Body* slender, streamlined; forehead depressed, sloping; lower jaw protruding; mouth large; dorsal fins high with considerable space between first and second.

Size: Maximum length 4.6 ft.; maximum weight 53.5 lb. [Florida records: conventional 44 lb. 3 oz.; fly fishing 30 lb. 4 oz.]

Diet: Fish (especially mullet) and crustaceans (shrimp and crabs).

Utilization: Banned-commercial; aquaculture; valued gamefish; excellent food fish, best fresh, doesn't keep well frozen.

Note: Spectacular jumper; taken by casting or trolling. Fish mangrove margins and channels before sunrise and just past sunset; under piers, large boats and shaded structures during daytime. Casts must not be too close or out of reach either, because Snook ambush rather than chase prey. Use surface flys and streamers, crankbaits resembling finger mullet or any live bait; rig with 30–50 test fluorocarbon leader (because of razor sharp cheek plates), wire leader will discourage strikes (see 'Fighting Robalo', p. 17 for details).

SWORDSPINE SNOOK

Centropomus ensiferus, FAMILY CENTROPOMIDAE (SNOOKS)

Description: *Color* silver; yellow-brown or yellow-green above; lighter silver-white below; lateral line beige, outlined in black, extending from top of gill cover through tail; pectoral and ventral fins yellow, other fins dusky brown. *Body* elongated; fins large; forehead slightly depressed, sloping; mouth large; lower jaw protruding; dorsal fins high with little space between first and second; second spine of anal fin greatly enlarged; scales largest of all snook.

Size: Maximum length 14.2 inches; maximum weight 2.3 lb.

Diet: Fish and shrimp; juveniles feed at mangrove shorelines, deeper canals and channels.

Utilization: Non-commercial; basically a sport fish (smallest and rarest of the four IRL snook species).

Note: Despite the smaller size, Swordspine Snook are good fighters. Light spinning, baitcasting or fly tackle; still fishing or casting. Use shrimp or minnows, small jigs, flies, topwater plugs, spoons, spinners or popping bugs; rig with nylon coated wire leader or heavy fluorocarbon leader (due to sharp gill covers).

TARPON SNOOK

Centropomus pectinatus, FAMILY CENTROPOMIDAE (SNOOKS)

Description: *Color* silver; yellow-green to green-brown above; lighter silver-white below; lateral line thin, black, extending from top of gill cover through tail; ventral fins yellowish. *Body* deep; forehead slightly depressed, sloping; lower jaw protruding, upturned; mouth large; dorsal fins high with little or no space between first and second; only snook with seven anal fin rays (others have six).

Size: Maximum length 22 inches; maximum weight 3.3 lb.

Diet: Primarily small fish, also shrimp and crabs.

Utilization: Non-commercial; basically a sport fish (decidedly smaller than the Common Snook).

Note: Good fighter. Light spinning, baitcasting or fly tackle; casting, still fishing or trolling. Use shrimp, baitfish such as Pilchards or Pinfish, small jigs, surface and diving plugs, spoons or streamer flies; rig with nylon coated wire leader or heavy fluorocarbon leader (due to sharp gill covers).

BLACK SEABASS

Centropristis striata, FAMILY SERRANIDAE (SEA BASSES, GROUPERS)

Description: *Color* highly variable, generally dark brown to black; dorsal fin with short white stripes; large males with iridescent blue or ebony markings; females with faint vertical bars. *Body* deep; topmost ridge of tail elongated when mature; tail occasionally with 3 lobes; gill cover with sharp posterior spine; dorsal fin with small flaps at spine tips; mature males often with hump in front of dorsal fin.

Size: Maximum length 26 inches; maximum weight 10.2 lb. [Florida records: conventional 5 lb. 1 oz.; fly fishing - vacant]

Diet: Favors crustaceans, also small fish, worms and molluscs.

Utilization: Commercial; aquarium, gamefish; excellent eating.

Note: Good fighter. Use squid, clams and small baitfish. Handle with care—sharp spines on dorsal fin.

GOLIATH GROUPER (JEWFISH)

Epinephelus itajara, FAMILY SERRANIDAE (SEA BASSES, GROUPERS)

Description: *Color* gray, green to brown-orange; head and fins covered with small black spots; sides with irregular dark vertical bars; juveniles tawny with irregular vertical banding. *Body* of mature adults extremely large with long head; pectoral and tail fins rounded; first dorsal fin shorter than, but not separated from, second dorsal; gill cover with 3 flat spines, middle one largest.

Size: Maximum length 8.2 ft.; maximum weight 981 lb. [Florida records: conventional 680 lb.; fly fishing 356 lb.]

Diet: Crustaceans (especially lobster), turtles, fish and rays.

Note: A docile creature easily overfished (primarily by spearfishing) and now totally protected in USA waters.

GAG

Mycteroperca microlepis, FAMILY SERRANIDAE (SEA BASSES)

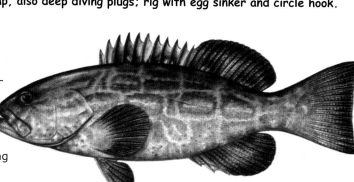

Description: *Color* light brownish gray with dark oval markings on side (look like kiss marks); fins darker; anal and tail fins have white margins. *Body* with strong serrated (saw-toothed) spur at back margin of cheek plate (more apparent in younger individuals).

Size: Maximum length 4.8 ft.; maximum weight 80.5 lb. [Florida records: conventional 80 lb. 6 oz.; fly fishing 9 lb. 4 oz.]

Diet: Mainly fish, also crabs, shrimp and squid; in IRL, juveniles (less than 8 inches) feed mainly on crustaceans that live in shallow grass beds.

Utilization: Highly commercial; gamefish; excellent food fish, best fresh (doesn't keep well frozen).

Note: Best grouper for fly fishing; mainly caught by bottom fishing and trolling along ICW. Use medium tackle with live or cut baitfish (Pinfish, grunts, Mojarra), squid or live shrimp, also deep diving plugs; rig with egg sinker and circle hook.

BLACK GROUPER

Mycteroperca bonaci, FAMILY SERRANIDAE (SEA BASSES)

Description: *Color* olive-brown to gray with sides having rectangular dark gray blotches and brassy spots; outer third of second dorsal, anal and tail fins black. *Body* deep; cheek plate gently rounded.

Size: Maximum length 59 inches; maximum weight 220 lb. [Florida records: conventional 113 lb. 6 oz.; fly fishing vacant]

Diet: Adults fish and squid; juveniles mainly crustaceans.

Utilization: Commercial; aquarium; gamefish; excellent high-quality food fish, best fresh (doesn't keep-well frozen).

Note: Medium tackle and chum. Use live or cut baitfish (Blue Runners, Pinfish, mullet), squid or fresh shrimp, also jigs and jigging spoons especially when tipped with natural bait; rig with egg sinker and circle hook.

RED GROUPER

Epinephelus morio, FAMILY SERRANIDAE (SEA BASSES)

Description: *Color* dark red-brown to rust above; pink to lighter red below; sides with whitish spots and large dark blotches. *Body* deep; gill cover with 3 flat spines, middle one largest.

Size: Maximum length 49 inches; maximum weight 50.7 lb. [Florida records: conventional 42 lb. 4 oz.; fly fishing 7 lb.]

Diet: Small fish and invertebrates.

Utilization: Commercial; aquarium; gamefish; excellent high-quality food fish, best fresh (doesn't keep well frozen).

Note: Medium tackle and chum. Use live or cut bait (particularly shrimp and crabs), squid or fresh shrimp, also jigs and jigging spoons, especially when tipped with natural bait; rig with 15–20 lb. test line, egg sinker and circle hook.

SCAMP

Mycteroperca phenax, FAMILY SERRANIDAE (SEA BASSES)

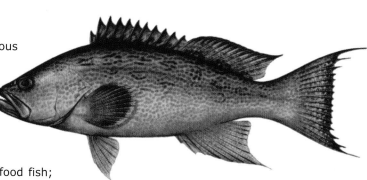

Description: *Color* dark tan to chocolate brown with numerous darker spots, dots or lines; outer margins of dorsal and tail fins darker. *Body* deep; upper and lower rays of tail fin elongated.

Size: Maximum length 42.1 inches; maximum weight 31.3 lb. [Florida records: conventional 28 lb. 6 oz.; fly fishing vacant]

Diet: Small fish, squid and crustaceans.

Utilization: Commercial; gamefish; excellent high-quality food fish; marketed fresh, salted or smoked.

Note: Light tackle and chum. Use live or cut baitfish, squid or fresh shrimp, also lead head jigs weighing 0.75-1.5 oz. tipped with natural bait; rig with 15–20 lb. test line, egg sinker and circle hook.

BLUEFISH

Pomatomus saltatrix, FAMILY POMATOMIDAE (BLUEFISHES)

Description: *Color* silver; blue to blue-green above; pectoral fin dark at base. *Body* long, streamlined; eyes large; mouth small; teeth prominent, sharp, slightly flattened, blade-like; scales small; lateral line straight; first dorsal fin short and low having 7–8 spines; second dorsal and anal fins opposite one another, approximately of equal size; tail deeply forked.

Size: Maximum length 51 inches; maximum weight 31.7 lb. [Florida records: conventional 22 lb. 2 oz.; fly fishing 18 lb.]

Diet: Small fish, crustaceans and shrimp; aggressive schooling species.

Utilization: Highly commercial; popular gamefish; good cut bait; small ones decent fresh (not good frozen), also smoked, dried or salted.

Note: Savage striker, strong fighter, any bait or lure. Casting, jigging, trolling and fly fishing. Use jigs, diving plugs, tubes and streamer flies, live bait preferred, dead or cut baits work; rig with 8-20 lb. test line and short wire leader. Handle with care, teeth are extremely sharp.

COBIA

Rachycentron canadum, FAMILY RACHYCENTRIDAE (COBIA)

Description: *Color* silver to dark brown; darker above; yellowish brown below; dark lateral stripe through eye to tail; juveniles with conspicuous alternating black and white horizontal stripes. *Body* long, cylindrical, torpedo-shaped; head broad and flat (shark-like); skin slick; lower jaw projects past upper jaw; first dorsal fin distinctive, formed as 7–9 short spines (not connected with membrane).

Size: Maximum length 6.5 ft.; maximum weight 150 lb. [Florida records: conventional 130 lb. 1 oz.; fly fishing 83 lb. 4 oz.]

Diet: Crabs, fish and squid.

Utilization: Minor commercial; gamefish; excellent food fish; marketed fresh, smoked or frozen.

Note: IRL inlets in summer; friendly fish that willingly take any large lure or live bait. Many neophyte anglers have passed them up because they look like sharks from above. Casting, spinning and fly fishing. Use diving plugs and jigs; bait preference depends on location (crabs, mullet, Pinfish); rig with 15-30 lb. test line.

BLUE RUNNER

Caranx crysos, FAMILY CARANGIDAE (JACKS AND POMPANOS)

Description: *Color* sliver; light blue-green to olive above; golden to silver-gray below; sides occasionally with faint bluish bars; gill cover often having black spot; tips of tail dark. *Body* tuna-like; upper jaw bone ending just below middle of eye; 45-46 bone-like projections (scutes) along straight part of lateral line; second dorsal and anal fins nearly identical with elongated tips.

Size: Maximum length 27.6 inches; maximum weight 11.1 lb. [IRL generally less than 1 lb.]

Diet: Fish, shrimp, squid and most invertebrates.

Utilization: Minor commercial; aquarium; pound-for-pound ranks among strongest gamefish; fair eating; good bait fish.

Note: Use light tackle with any type of rapidly worked small lure or bait.

CREVALLE JACK (JACK CREVALLE)

Caranx hippos, FAMILY CARANGIDAE (JACKS AND POMPANOS)

Description: *Color* silver; blue, green or blue-green metallic luster above; lighter below; black spot on upper margin of gill covers (parallel with eye); large dark oval blotch on lower part of pectoral fins; occasionally tail and underside yellowish. *Body* deep; head large, blunt; no scales on throat; second dorsal and anal fins nearly identical with elongated tips; tail widely forked, sickle-shaped.

Size: Maximum length 4 ft.; maximum weight 70.5 lb. [Florida records: conventional 57 lb.; fly fishing 37 lb. 8 oz.]

Diet: Smaller fish, shrimp and other invertebrates.

Utilization: Commercial; aquarium; gamefish; marketed fresh or smoked; eaten pan-fried, broiled and baked, best when dark-red lateral-line flesh removed.

Note: Aggressive feeder with powerful crushing jaws; grunts and croaks when caught. Fights from the leverage of its side instead of making long runs; 25+ pounders are often called 'hour jacks', because it takes an hour to land one. Use light tackle; watch for schools chopping at baitfish and drift into the frenzy; will take any artificial worked fast or live baitfish.

PALOMETA

Trachinotus goodei, FAMILY CARANGIDAE (JACKS AND POMPANOS)

Description: *Color* silver; bluish silver to gray above; yellow below; four narrow dark bars on upper sides. *Body* deep, compressed; snout blunt; first dorsal fin as six independent spines; second dorsal and anal fins nearly identical with long, dark (margins often black) tips extending well beyond base of tail; tail deeply forked.

Size: Maximum length 19.7 inches; maximum weight 1.2 lb.

Diet: Crustaceans, polychaete worms, molluscs and fish.

Utilization: Minor commercial; gamefish.

Note: Feisty battler on ultralight or fly fishing tackle. Use small artificial lures, flies or pieces of shrimp or baitfish.

PERMIT

Trachinotus falcatus, FAMILY CARANGIDAE (JACKS AND POMPANOS)

Description: *Color* reflective (like a mirror) silver; dark or iridescent blue to blue-green above; gold, yellow or orange tint below; occasionally with dark blotch behind pectoral fin. *Body* deep, compressed; snout blunt; first dorsal fin as six independent spines; second dorsal and anal fins nearly identical with long, dark tips not extending beyond base of tail; tail deeply forked.

Size: Maximum length 4 ft.; maximum weight 79.4 lb. [Florida records: conventional 56 lb. 2 oz.; fly fishing 41 lb. 8 oz.]

Diet: Molluscs, crabs, shrimp, urchins and small fish; juveniles eat small invertebrates.

Utilization: Aquarium; gamefish; excellent food fish.

Note: Permit hold in deep water over wrecks and structure but feed on shallow seagrass flats. Uncommon but present in summer on the southernmost IRL flats. The most difficult flats quarry to hook and land on fly tackle—just another jack when taken in deeper water; use live crabs and specialized crab-fly patterns (see Billy-the-Crab pattern on pp. 16-17).

FLORIDA POMPANO

Trachinotus carolinus, FAMILY CARANGIDAE (JACKS AND POMPANOS)

Description: *Color* silver; darker green-gray to blue-green above; lighter or yellowish below. *Body* deep, compressed (slightly flattened); mouth small; snout blunt; first dorsal fin of 5–6 independent short spines; second dorsal and anal fins nearly identical with elongated tips.

Size: Maximum length 25 inches; maximum weight 8.3 lb. [Florida records: conventional 8 lb. 4 oz.; fly fishing 6 lb. 8 oz.]

Diet: Molluscs, shrimp, crabs, various other invertebrates (mostly a bottom feeder), rarely small fish.

Utilization: Highly commercial; aquarium; excellent food fish. Highest priced saltwater fish in US markets.

Note: Light tackle; bottom, casting or drift techniques (common in deep holes near inlets). Use live bait [live Sand Flea Crab best] or small shrimp-tipped jigs; look for water temperature above 70°F. A good homemade jig that imitates the Sand Crab can be made from a dead 'olive seashell', found in IRL dredge spoil.

LOOKDOWN

Selene vomer, FAMILY CARANGIDAE (JACKS AND POMPANOS)

Description: *Color* silver, iridescent, occasionally with brassy, gold, green, blue or purple highlights; often with 3–4 pale vertical bars. *Body* deep, compressed (very flat), extremely thin; face and forehead flattened vertically, blunt; eyes large; scales smooth; lateral line arched toward front; second dorsal and anal fins nearly identical with extremely long tapering tips often trailing past tail.

Size: Maximum length 19 inches; maximum weight 4.6 lb.

Diet: Small crabs, shrimp, fish and worms.

Utilization: Minor commercial; aquarium; gamefish; marketed fresh; excellent food fish.

Note: A fish of opportunity. Ultralight tackle. Use live anchovies or small shiny inline spinners.

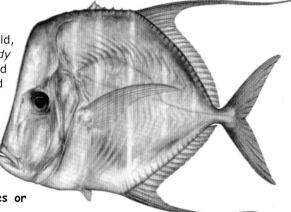

LEATHERJACKET (LEATHER JACK)

Oligoplites saurus, FAMILY CARANGIDAE (JACKS AND POMPANOS)

Description: *Color* silver; bluish above; lighter below; tail yellow. *Body* slender, compressed; scales needle-like, embedded in leathery skin; lateral line nearly straight (slightly arched over pectoral fin); dorsal fin of five separate spines; dorsal and anal spines have venomous glands that can inflict painful wounds.

Size: Maximum length 13.8 inches; maximum weight 10.1 oz.

Diet: Fish and crustaceans.

Utilization: Poor baitfish; marketed salted/dried in some countries; considered a third-rate food fish.

Note: Like a small mackerel, with none of the redeeming features; nasty spines, do not touch. Light or ultralight tackle; either casting or still fishing. Use live baitfish and shrimp or small jigs and plugs.

ATLANTIC BUMPER

Chloroscombrus chrysurus, FAMILY CARANGIDAE (JACKS AND POMPANOS)

Description: *Color* silver; metallic blue above; silver to golden below; black saddle spot at upper base of tail; gill cover with small black area on posterior edge. *Body* deep but narrow; lower (belly) profile more strongly curved than upper (back) profile; lateral line more strongly arched toward front.

Size: Maximum length 2 ft. [IRL generally about 1 ft. long]

Diet: Fish, squid, octopus, zooplankton and detritus.

Utilization: Commercial; baitfish; marketed fresh or salted.

Note: Caught by cast net.

TRIPLETAIL

Lobotes surinamensis, FAMILY LOBOTIDAE (TRIPLETAILS)

Description: *Color* mottled dark brown or dark green-yellow above, silver-gray below; pectoral fins pale yellow; tail fin with yellow margin. *Body* deep, somewhat rounded; head slightly concave above eyes; second dorsal and anal fins large, rounded and extending rearward (resembling rounded tails, hence "Tripletail").

Size: Maximum length 43 inches; maximum weight 42.3 lb. [Florida records: conventional 40 lb. 13 oz.; fly fishing 21 lb. 2 oz.]

Diet: Benthic crustaceans and small fish.

Utilization: Commercial; gamefish; excellent high quality food fish; marketed fresh, frozen or salted.

Note: Medium to lightweight casting tackle; in shade under floating debris, weedlines, buoys or navigational structures. Use live or cut baitfish, squid or fresh shrimp, also streamer flies, plastic and bucktail jigs, mirror plugs.

CUBERA SNAPPER

Lutjanus cyanopterus, FAMILY LUTJANIDAE (SNAPPERS)

Description: *Color* dark gray with reddish tinge above; lighter below; dorsal and tail fins gray; anal and ventral fins red; pectoral fins translucent or gray. *Body* somewhat deep; lips thick; scales on back in oblique rows above lateral line. Very similar to Gray Snapper which has arrow-shaped (with a shaft) patch of teeth on roof of mouth; Cubera have arrow-shaped (without shaft) tooth patch like an inverted V.

Size: Maximum length 63 inches; maximum weight 126 lb. [Florida records: conventional 116 lb.; fly fishing vacant]

Diet: Fish, lobster, shrimp and crabs.

Utilization: Commercial; gamefish; smaller fish good eating, larger ones tough, not particularly good.

Note: Moves into inlets occasionally, smaller individuals confused with Gray (Mangrove) Snapper. Heavy to medium tackle. Whole live lobster best bait, will also take Blue Crabs or live baitfish.

DOG SNAPPER

Lutjanus jocu, FAMILY LUTJANIDAE (SNAPPERS)

Description: *Color* olive brown with bronze tinge, occasionally with narrow pale bars; lower sides and belly light reddish with copper tinge; horizontal blue line below eye in juveniles, blue dots in adults; distinctive light triangular bar between eye and rear of mouth. *Body* deep, stout; two large canine teeth in upper jaw (fang-like), visible even when mouth is closed.

Size: Maximum length 4.2 ft.; maximum weight 63 lb.

Diet: Fish and benthic invertebrates, including shrimp, crabs, snails and squid.

Utilization: Commercial; aquarium; not particularly good eating.

Note: Light to medium weight tackle. Use live bait (Ballyhoo or squid), jigs or jigging spoons; rig with 30 lb. test line.

MANGROVE SNAPPER (GRAY SNAPPER)

Lutjanus griseus, FAMILY LUTJANIDAE (SNAPPERS)

Description: *Color* dark brown or gray with rows of red or orange spots along sides; dorsal fin with black or reddish border; juveniles with dark horizontal bands from snout through eyes, often with blue lines on cheeks below eyes. *Body* deep; head slightly concave above eyes; snout long, pointed; two conspicuous canine teeth at front of upper jaw.

Size: Maximum length 35 inches; maximum weight 44 lb.; maximum age 21 years. [Florida records: conventional 17 lb.; fly fishing 10 lb. 12 oz.]

Diet: Small fish, shrimp, crabs, gastropods, squid, octopus and some zooplankton; generally feed at night.

Utilization: Commercial; aquarium; good food fish; marked fresh or frozen.

Note: Found next to mangroves, in canals, channels and patch reefs; a leader-shy schooling fish that is easiest to fool just after dark on a free-lined live shrimp; also use live Pinfish or cut Ballyhoo; seldom caught on artificials.

LANE SNAPPER

Lutjanus synagris, FAMILY LUTJANIDAE (SNAPPERS)

Description: *Color* pink to red with green tinge and faint dark vertical bars; silver with yellow tinge below; sides with 8–10 horizontal yellow or gold stripes; one black spot above lateral line and below middle portion of dorsal fin; outer margin of tail dark to black. *Body* moderately compressed, relatively deep.

Size: Maximum length 23.6 inches; maximum weight 7.8 lb. [Florida records: conventional 6 lb. 6 oz.; fly fishing vacant]

Diet: Small fish, crabs, shrimp, worms, gastropods, squid and octopus.

Utilization: Commercial; aquarium; panfish; excellent food fish.

Note: A fish of deeper Turtle Grass beds. Position boat on edge of grass/hard bottom interface to increase diversity of action. Use live shrimp or cut bait on jig head (or egg sinker/circle-hook rig) in chum line.

MUTTON SNAPPER

Lutjanus analis, FAMILY LUTJANIDAE (SNAPPERS)

Description: *Color* olive green, silver, gray, red-brown to maroon; darker above; whitish with red tinge below; small black spot on upper back just above lateral line and below anterior dorsal fin; pair of blue stripes on snout-cheek region, upper stripe runs through eye to gill cover margin; lower fins and tail with red tinge; may darken or lighten rapidly. *Body* oblong, relatively deep, moderately compressed; dorsal and anal fins pointed.

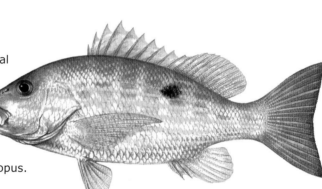

Size: Maximum length 37 inches; maximum weight 34.4 lb.; maximum age 14 years. [Florida records: conventional 30 lb. 4 oz.; fly fishing 17 lb.]

Diet: Fish, shrimp, crabs, squid and gastropods.

Utilization: Highly commercial; gamefish; excellent food fish.

Note: The wariest of fish when in skinny water; generally in deeper Turtle Grass beds; highly prized by flats fly anglers, but rarely caught. Position boat on edge of grass/hard bottom interface to increase diversity of action. Use live shrimp or cut bait on egg sinker rig (or jig head) in chum line.

SCHOOLMASTER SNAPPER

Lutjanus apodus, FAMILY LUTJANIDAE (SNAPPERS)

Description: *Color* olive gray to brown with yellow tinge; head occasionally with reddish tinge; juveniles with eight pale narrow vertical bars, faint or absent in adults; solid or broken blue line running under eye, also faint or absent in adults; fins yellow. *Body* deep; snout long, pointed; mouth large; one canine tooth notably enlarged, visible when mouth is closed; pectoral fins long.

Size: Maximum length 26.5 inches; maximum weight 23.8 lb.

Diet: Fish, shrimp, crabs, worms, gastropods and squid.

Utilization: Commercial; fair food fish; marketed fresh or frozen.

Note: Found next to mangroves, in canals, channels and patch reefs. Use live Pinfish or cut Ballyhoo; seldom caught on artificials.

SHEEPSHEAD

Archosargus probatocephalus, FAMILY SPARIDAE (PORGIES)

Description: *Color* silver, often with yellow tint; 5–6 distinct dark to black vertical bars on sides. *Body* deep, compressed; upper profile strongly arched; teeth prominent; dorsal and anal fins with strong, sharp spines.

Size: Maximum length 3 ft.; maximum weight 21.2 lb. [Florida records: conventional 15 lb. 2 oz.; fly fishing 7 lb. 4 oz.]

Diet: Molluscs (oysters) and crustaceans (fiddler crabs and barnacles); well-known for nibbling at bait.

Utilization: Commercial; aquarium; excellent food fish; marketed fresh or frozen.

Note: A deadly technique is to collect massive oyster communities (see regulations) from seawalls, break them up over a hole or channel next to a grassbed or mangrove bank. Use oyster meat or associated crab fauna as bait; live shrimp work reasonably well; rig with small hook; generally not taken on artificials.

GRASS PORGY

Calamus arctifrons, FAMILY SPARIDAE (PORGIES)

Description: *Color* pale tan to silver; dark olive above; white below; dark bar across forehead extends through eyes to corners of mouth; dark spot on lateral line just behind gill opening; dark blotches on body in 5–8 vertical and 4 horizontal indistinct series; dark V at base of tail; tail with smaller dark bars or dashes. *Body* moderately compressed, belly with distinct keel; lower jaw with pointed tip that fits into v-shaped notch in upper jaw.

Size: Maximum length 10 inches; maximum weight 1 lb.

Diet: Invertebrates.

Utilization: Commercial; baitfish; marketed fresh or frozen.

Note: Light tackle. Use live or dead shrimp or cut bait.

PINFISH

Lagodon rhomboides, FAMILY SPARIDAE (PORGIES)

Description: *Color* bluish to greenish silver; horizontal stripes blue and orange-yellow or bronze; vertical bars 4–6, dark; fins yellow; black spot behind gill cover centered on lateral line. *Body* relatively deep: mouth small; teeth incisor-like.

Size: Maximum length 15.7 inches; maximum weight 3.3 lb.

Diet: Algae, crustaceans, molluscs, worms and occasionally small fish that are associated with seagrass habitats; omnivorous when young, mostly herbivorous as adults.

Utilization: Minor commercial; mostly baitfish; popular as durable and lively bait.

Note: Important to the health of seagrass beds (along with mullet), since a large part of their diet is algae they help keep harmful epiphyte loads on seagrasses in check. Use traps, ultralight tackle with chum or cast nets.

WEAKFISH

Cynoscion regalis, FAMILY SCIAENIDAE (DRUMS OR CROAKERS)

Description: *Color* tints of blue, purple, lavender, gold and copper; dark olive or blue-green above; irregular rows of ill-defined dark spots above lateral line; tip of tongue with black margin; ventral and anal fins yellow; pectoral fins olive on outside, yellow to silver white underneath. *Body* streamlined (similar to freshwater trout); canine teeth 1–2, prominent, at tip of upper jaw.

Size: Maximum length 38.6 inches; maximum weight 19.5 lb. [Florida records: conventional 10 lb.; fly fishing vacant]

Diet: Shrimp, crabs, molluscs and small fish.

Utilization: Commercial; aquarium; excellent food fish; marketed fresh or frozen.

Note: Techniques for Spotted Seatrout (see previous page) also apply to this species. The name 'Weakfish' refers to the tender mouth (hooks are easily ripped out, so use a delicate touch and light drag).

SPOT

Leiostomus xanthurus, FAMILY SCIAENIDAE (DRUMS OR CROAKERS)

Description: *Color* brass; blue to brown above, silver to white below; shoulders with distinct brown spot; upper body with 12–15 narrow diagonal dark lines. *Body* short, deep; back high; mouth low, horizontal; tail slightly forked.

Size: Maximum length 14.1 inches; maximum weight 1 lb. [Florida records: conventional vacant; fly fishing vacant]

Diet: Worms, small crustaceans and organic detritus.

Utilization: Commercial; baitfish; popular panfish.

Note: Caught by still fishing.

GULF FLOUNDER

Paralichthys albigutta, FAMILY PARALICHTHYIDAE (LARGE-TOOTH FLOUNDERS)

Description: *Color* brown to gray, can darken or lighten rapidly to match bottom color; numerous dark and light blotches; three prominent eye-like spots forming triangle on top side, middle spot on lateral line; bottom side white, nondescript. *Body* flattened with both eyes on upper side (generally left side); lateral line arched above pectoral fin.

Size: Maximum length 27.9 inches; maximum weight 6.2 lb.

Diet: Crustaceans, small mullet or other bait fish.

Utilization: Minor commercial; excellent eating when fresh.

Note: Often congregates at IRL impoundment culverts during high outgoing tides. Best sport on light tackle; rig with light egg sinker; use finger mullet, shrimp, minnows and fiddler crabs, on or close to the bottom. Not easily caught on lures.

SOUTHERN FLOUNDER

Paralichthys lethostigma, FAMILY PARALICHTHYIDAE (LARGE-TOOTH FLOUNDERS)

Description: *Color* brown to olive, can darken or lighten rapidly to match bottom color; numerous diffuse dark and light blotches; bottom side white, nondescript. *Body* flattened with both eyes on upper side (generally left side); lateral line with very high arch above pectoral fin.

Size: Maximum length 32.7 inches; maximum weight 20.6 lb. [Florida records for all types of flounder: conventional 20 lb. 9 oz.; fly fishing 2 lb. 9 oz.]

Diet: Fish, crabs and shrimp. Follows fall Silver Mullet run into IRL. Juveniles mainly eat small bottom invertebrates.

Utilization: Minor commercial; gamefish; marketed fresh or frozen.

Note: Fish bridges, jetties and near inlets on high outgoing tides with medium-light tackle. Use finger mullet, shrimp, minnows and fiddler crabs, on or close to the bottom; rig with light egg sinker. Not easily caught on lures.

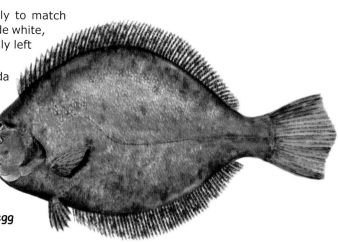

HARDHEAD CATFISH

Arius felis, FAMILY ARIIDAE (SEA CATFISHES)

Description: *Color* silver to gray-green; dark brown to dark blue above; white to yellowish below. *Body* with four chin barbels and barbels at corners of mouth; lengthwise groove in depression from middle of head to between eyes.

Size: Maximum length 27.6 inches; maximum weight 12.1 lb. [Florida records: conventional 3 lb. 5 oz.; fly fishing 2 lb. 8 oz.]

Diet: Scavenger, feeding on carrion.

Utilization: Minor commercial; panfish; marginally edible, but generally not consumed.

Note: Caught from catwalks, bridges and piers. When these appear, it's time to change location.

GAFFTOPSAIL CATFISH (SAIL CAT)

Bagre marinus, FAMILY ARIIDAE (SEA CATFISHES)

Description: *Color* gray-blue to dark brown above; silver below; belly white; anal fin white to pale blue. *Body* with distinctive barbels extending from corner of mouth (flattened band-like projections of skin) and one pair of chin barbels; first ray of dorsal fin and first ray of pectoral fin elongated, flat, filament-like; dorsal and pectoral fins with venomous serrated (saw-toothed) erect spines.

Size: Maximum length 27.1 inches; maximum weight 9.6 lb. [Florida records: conventional 8 lb. 14 oz.; fly fishing 7 lb. 8 oz.]

Diet: Small fish, invertebrates (shrimp and crabs) and carrion; scavenger.

Utilization: Commercial; panfish; marketed fresh; flesh considered good but not eaten much in USA; skin produces extraordinary quantities of slime.

Note: Caught on bottom from boats, piers and catwalks. Prefers live bait; also taken on cut bait, light plugs and lures.

ATLANTIC SPADEFISH

Chaetodipterus faber, FAMILY EPHIPPIDAE (SPADEFISHES, BATFISHES AND SCATS)

Description: *Color* pale gray to silver with 4–6 irregular, bold, blackish, vertical bars; bars fade with age; juveniles generally jet black. *Body* very deep, flattened, compressed, disk-shaped; snout blunt; mouth small; dorsal and ventral fins nearly identical, both with elongated tips.

Size: Maximum length 36 inches; maximum weight 20 lb. [IRL about 2 lb.]

Diet: Benthic invertebrates (crustaceans, molluscs, worms, corals) as well as plankton; feeds on tentacles of jellyfish.

Utilization: Minor commercial; aquarium; good eating when fresh.

Note: Around piers, jetties, bridges and causeways. Light to medium tackle. A nibbler, use cut bait and pieces of shrimp; rig with small hooks.

FANTAIL MULLET (SILVER MULLET)

Mugil gyrans, FAMILY MUGILIDAE (MULLETS)

Description: *Color* silver; blue, green or blue-green metallic tints above; lighter below; anal and ventral fins often yellowish; dark spot often present at base of pectoral fin; tail with darkish margin. *Body* torpedo-shaped; second dorsal fin located over anal fin.

Size: Maximum length 18 inches; maximum weight 1 lb.

Diet: Algae, small crustaceans and detritus.

Utilization: Bait, live or cut.

Note: Massive southward migrations along beaches in fall; important to the health of seagrasses (along with Striped Mullet and Pinfish), since they help keep harmful epiphyte loads in check. Caught with cast net.

STRIPED MULLET (BLACK OR FLATHEAD MULLET)

Mugil cephalus, FAMILY MUGILIDAE (MULLETS)

Description: *Color* silver; olive-green to blue-gray above; white below; faint horizontal black stripes; occasionally with faint dark vertical bars. *Body* elongated, irregularly torpedo-shaped; top profile straighter; bottom profile deeper; snout blunt; mouth small; first dorsal fin with 5 spines; second dorsal fin with 8 soft rays.

Size: Maximum length 48 inches; maximum weight 17.6 lb.

Diet: Attached algae while in estuaries or fresh water, otherwise benthic organisms and detritus; mainly a bottom feeder.

Utilization: Highly commercial; aquarium; baitfish; marketed fresh, salted, dried or frozen; roe sold fresh or smoked.

Note: Along with shrimp, the major prey of carnivorous fish in the IRL. Frequent leapers in nature but, interestingly, not when hooked. Important to the health of seagrasses (along with Pinfish), since they help keep harmful epiphyte loads in check. Caught with cast net, also hook and line using doughballs.

STRIPED MOJARRA (SAND PERCH)

Diapterus plumieri, FAMILY GERREIDAE (MOJARRAS)

Description: *Color* tan to silver; dark olive above; lighter below; often with metallic sheen; each scale row on back and sides with black stripe along center; all fins except pectoral dusky in adults; anal fin sometimes dark orange. *Body* compressed; moderately deep; dorsal and anal spines long, stout.

Size: Maximum length 15.7 inches; maximum weight 2.3 lb.

Diet: Bits of dead shellfish, crustaceans, small bivalves.

Utilization: Minor commercial; baitfish (terrific 'cuda' bait); not palatable, processed into fishmeal.

Note: Caught with cast net or light tackle with bits of shrimp.

STRIPED ANCHOVY

Anchoa hepsetu, FAMILY ENGRAULIDAE (ANCHOVIES)

Description: *Color* gray to transparent silver; greenish above; head often yellowish; silver horizontal side stripe of uniform width; dark line above stripe. *Body* with pointed snout; anal fin origin below midpoint of dorsal fin.

Size: Maximum length 6 inches.

Diet: Gastropods (snails), foraminiferans (microscopic animals with shells) and occasionally mysids or worms; juveniles eat zooplantkton (suspended microscopic animals), primarily copepods.

Utilization: Minor commercial; usually as bait, delicate.

Note: Caught with cast net.

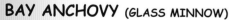

BAY ANCHOVY (GLASS MINNOW)

Anchoa mitchilli, FAMILY ENGRAULIDAE (ANCHOVIES)

Description: *Color* grayish to transparent silver with narrow silver side stripe; stripe often faint or absent toward front. *Body* variable, but generally slender; snout blunt; lower jaw long, tip pointed, reaching almost to gill opening.

Size: Maximum length 4 inches.

Diet: Mysid shrimp and plankton (copepods), to a lesser extent fish, gastropods and isopods (small jointed crustaceans).

Utilization: Minor commercial; usually as bait, occasionally to make anchovy paste.

Note: Caught with cast net.

GREAT BARRACUDA (CUDA)

Sphyraena barracuda

FAMILY SPHYRAENIDAE (BARRACUDAS)

Description: *Color* silver gray; darker greenish above; lighter below; lower sides usually with irregular small black blotches; upper sides with 18–22 diagonal dark bars (not always apparent); back and blotches become olive-green camouflaged when fish assumes ambush mode; tail dark, often with white tips; juveniles with dark stripe on sides. *Body* long, slender; lower jaw extending well beyond upper jaw; top of head between eyes flat or concave; mouth large; eyes large; snout pointed; teeth sharp and numerous; powerful tail [bracket-shaped (})].

Size: Maximum length 6.5 ft.; maximum weight 110 lb. [Florida records: conventional 67 lb.; fly fishing 37 lb. 12 oz.]

Diet: Fish (particularly Needlefish), squid and shrimp. Along with sharks, the top predator in most of their habitats.

Utilization: Aquarium; gamefish; marketed fresh, salted or smoked (large specimens concentrate toxic ciguatoxin).

Note: Blue water to backwaters. Ambush predator that will readily give chase. Must use short wire leader for this toothy antagonist; an exciting jumping fish that cannot resist a struggling live baitfish, iridescent blue tube-flies or any silver lure; taken by casting or trolling. This species is often ciguatoxic; juveniles not as poisonous and are eaten throughout Caribbean Central America. Rarely attacks humans (known to slash at shiny objects in murky waters).

CERO (CERO MACKEREL)

Scomberomorus regalis

FAMILY SCOMBRIDAE (MACKERELS, TUNAS, BONITOS)

Description: *Color* silver; iridescent blue-green above; long mid-lateral bronze stripe with rows of small yellow to yellow-orange streaks and spots above and below; front part of first dorsal fin blue-black or black. *Body* long, slender; lateral line gently curving, terminating where body meets tail; scales small.

Size: Maximum length 48 inches; maximum weight 18 lb. [Florida records: conventional 17 lb. 2 oz.; fly fishing 9 lb.]

Diet: Small fish (herrings, sardines, menhaden, anchovies), squid and shrimp.

Utilization: Minor commercial; excellent food and gamefish; marketed fresh or smoked.

Note: Fish deeper waters near inlets and drop-offs during winter; trolling, chumming and casting; expect screaming high speed runs; for success you need a very light touch due to the fragile mouth structure. Use live bait or bucktail jig head tipped with whole shrimp; rig with short nylon coated wire leader.

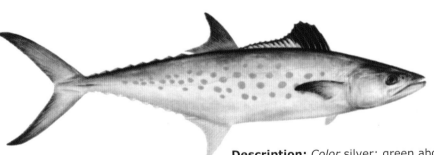

SPANISH MACKEREL

Scomberomorus maculatus

FAMILY SCOMBRIDAE (MACKERELS, TUNAS, BONITOS)

Description: *Color* silver; green above; sides with three rows of round, elliptical or irregular orange to yellow spots; front part of first dorsal fin blue-black or black. *Body* long, slender; lateral line gently curving, terminating where body meets tail; scales small.

Size: Maximum length 36 inches; maximum weight 13 lb. [Florida records: conventional 12 lb.; fly fishing 6 lb. 13 oz.]

Diet: Small fish (herrings, shads, sardines, menhadens, anchovies), shrimp and squid.

Utilization: Minor commercial; good food and gamefish; marketed fresh, frozen or smoked; more-oily flesh than Cero.

Note: Once the major commercial export fish in the early history of the IRL. Use light tackle in deeper water near inlets and drop-offs; trolling, chumming and casting; expect fast runs and hard fight; when large winter schools are encountered, action is fast and furious. Use small shiny metal lures, small baitfish-patterned flys or live bait such as shrimp or small silvery baitfish; rig with short nylon coated wire leader.

Common Shore Birds and Mammals of the Indian River Lagoon

ROSEATE SPOONBILL

Ajaia ajaja, FAMILY THRESKIORNITHIDAE (IBISES AND SPOONBILLS)

Description: *Body* white and pink; head and neck white; wings and sides brilliant pink; tail orange; shoulders often crimson; bill long, flat with broad spoon-like tip; legs red; feet blackish. *Juveniles* pale pink and white. *Flies* with neck and legs extended.

Size: 30–34 inches tall; wing span to 4.4 ft.

Habitat: Mangroves, brackish marshes and saltwater lagoons; in small flocks.

Nest: In dense bushes and low trees; built of sticks; in colonies; eggs 2–3, dull white with dark spots and blotches.

Diet: Shrimp, small fish, snails and crabs; forage by rhythmically sweeping spoon shaped bills from side to side, locating prey by touch.

Note: Pink coloration derived from algal carotinoid pigments taken up by shrimp. Historically populations were decimated by plume hunters, but populations are now on the increase.

WOOD STORK (WOOD IBIS)

Mycteria americana, FAMILY CICONIIDAE (STORKS)

Description: *Body* white, large; head and neck featherless, dark gray; flight feathers and tail black; bill long, stout, slightly curved, black in adults, dull yellow in juveniles; legs black to blue-gray; feet pink; flies with neck and legs extended.

Size: 35–45 inches tall; wing span to 5.5 ft.

Habitat: Marshes, mudflats, lagoons and estuaries; breeding chiefly in cypress swamps; occasionally mangroves.

Nest: In trees; built as huge stick platforms; in enormous colonies numbering up to 10,000 pairs; eggs 2–3, white.

Diet: Fish, crustaceans and snakes; shuffles feet to startle prey then locates with sensitive bill.

Note: Numbers have declined drastically in recent years from loss of habitat due to development, logging and destruction of wetlands.

GREAT EGRET

Ardea alba, FAMILY ARDEIDAE (HERONS AND EGRETS)

Description: *Body* large, entirely white; bill bright yellow; legs black; breeding plumage has long lacy feathers on back and lower foreneck

(the similar, but smaller, Snowy Egret has black bill, black legs and yellow feet). *Flies* with neck folded and legs extended.

Size: 35–41 inches tall; wing span to 4.6 ft.

Habitat: Freshwater and saltwater marshes, marshy ponds, lagoons and tidal flats.

Nest: In trees or bushes; built as platform of sticks; in colonies, often with other species of herons; eggs 3–7, pale greenish-blue.

Diet: Fish, frogs, reptiles and crayfish.

Note: Other common names: American Egret, Common Egret, Large Egret, White Egret, Great White Egret and Great White Heron. Historically, decimated by plume hunters; still in danger due to destruction of wetlands.

SNOWY EGRET

Egretta thula, FAMILY ARDEIDAE (HERONS AND EGRETS)

Description: *Body* small, delicate, entirely white; bill slender, black; legs black; feet bright yellow; when breeding has long lacy plumes on head, neck and back. *Juveniles* similar to

adults, but lack plumes and have yellow stripe up back of leg (similar to Cattle Egret which has pale bill, legs and feet). *Flies* with neck folded and legs extended.

Size: 20–27 inches tall; wing span to 3.2 ft.

Habitat: Marshes, ponds, swamps and mud flats.

Nest: In bushes, reeds or on ground; built as platform of sticks; singly or in colonies, often with other species of herons; eggs 3–5, pale blue-green.

Diet: Feeds by sprinting rapidly through shallow water, chasing schools of panicked minnows and shrimp (see also p. 21).

Note: Often found cooperatively feeding in small groups.

REDDISH EGRET

Egretta rufescens, FAMILY ARDEIDAE (HERONS AND EGRETS)

Description: *Body* medium-size, slate-gray; head and neck cinnamon (rufous), shaggy; legs dark blue-gray; bill pink with dark tip; white phase has bluish legs, pink bill with dark tip [Little Blue Heron darker, without shaggy neck, with gray (not pink) bill]. *Immature* grayish with buff on head, neck and wings; bill dark. *Flies* with neck folded and legs extended.

Size: 26–32 inches tall; wing span to 3.8 ft.

Habitat: Salt and brackish water estuaries; breeding along shallow bays and lagoons.

Nest: In mangroves or low bushes; built of sticks, occasionally on ground; eggs 3–4, pale blue-green.

Diet: Fish, frogs and crustaceans; forages by moving rapidly about the shallows with its wings raised, chasing down spooked prey, often brings wings forward in front of its body, creating a shady glare-free patch to spot prey more easily.

Note: A white form of this species exists but is rare.

AMERICAN AVOCET

Recurvirostra americana, FAMILY RECURVIROSTRIDAE (STILTS AND AVOCETS)

Description: *Body* with upperparts and wings patterned in black and white; underparts white; head and neck rich buff-cinnamon in summer, grayish-white in winter; legs long, gray-blue; feet gray-blue; bill slender, black, upturned. *Flies* with neck and legs extended.

Size: 16–20 inches tall.

Habitat: Marshes, shallow marshy lakes, estuaries, shallow lagoons and coastal ponds.

Nest: Often in loose colonies; on beach or mudflats; in shallow depression sparsely lined with grass; eggs 4, olive-buff.

Diet: Small crustaceans, aquatic insects and floating seeds.

Note: Avocets feed much like spoonbills, sweeping their bills from side to side along the surface of the mud. In the 19th century, they were hunted to near-extinction. Recently given complete protection, they seem to be gaining in numbers.

GLOSSY IBIS

Plegadis falcinellus, FAMILY THRESKIORNITHIDAE (IBISES)

Description: *Body* large; plumage chestnut with metallic purple gloss in breeding season, dark metallic green in winter; head and neck streaked; bill dark, down-curved; wings glossy greenish; eyes brown; face featherless, outlined by thin white line, skin dark; legs reddish to gray-brown. *Flies* with both neck and legs extended.

Size: 22–26 inches tall; wing span to 3.1 ft.

Habitat: Salt and brackish water estuaries; breeding along shallow bays and lagoons.

Nesting: In bushes or trees, rarely on ground; built of sticks; in colonies, often along with herons; eggs 3–4, pale blue-green.

Diet: Crabs, insects and snakes.

WHITE IBIS

Eudocimus albus, FAMILY THRESKIORNITHIDAE (IBISES)

Description: *Body* white; wing tips black (usually hidden at rest); face and down-curved bill pink to red; legs slate-gray, red in breeding season. *Juveniles* brown above and white below; bill and legs brown. *Flies* with neck and legs extended.

Size: 23–28 inches tall; wing span to 3.2 ft.

Habitat: Marshes, mudflats, lagoons and estuaries; gregarious, in small flocks.

Nest: In low trees and bushes over water; built of sticks; in colonies; eggs 3–4, greenish-white with dark spots or blotches.

Diet: Crabs, worms, molluscs and small fish.

Note: White Ibis help increase fish populations by preying on certain crab species that eat fish eggs.

TRICOLORED HERON (LOUISIANA HERON)

Egretta tricolor, FAMILY ARDEIDAE (HERONS AND EGRETS)

Description: *Body* slender, gray-blue; bill yellowish with dark tip; neck rusty gray; rump and belly white. Flies with neck folded and legs extended.

Size: 25–30 inches tall; wing span to 3.2 ft.

Habitat: Swamps, lakes, salt marshes, mangrove islands, mudflats and lagoons.

Nest: In trees, reeds or on ground; built of sticks; eggs 3–4, blue-green.

Diet: Frogs and fish.

Note: Despite its relatively small size, it forages in fairly deep water, often with legs completely submerged.

GREEN HERON

Butorides virescens, FAMILY ARDEIDAE (HERONS AND EGRETS)

Description: *Body* blackish green; crown blackish green; back and wings dark gray-green or gray-blue; face, neck and chest rusty gray to dark chestnut; white stripe from throat down foreneck, streaked with dark brown; bill dark; legs bright orange. *Juveniles* have streaks on neck, breast, and sides. *Flies* with neck folded and legs extended.

Size: 16–22 inches tall.

Habitat: Marshes, lakes, mangroves and estuaries; breeds mainly in freshwater or brackish marshes.

Nest: In low trees and dense thickets; built of loose sticks; eggs 3–6, pale green or pale blue.

Diet: Insects, frogs and small fish; forages along edges of mangroves and estuaries.

Note: Green Herons stretch their neck and bill forward, taking aim and with a quick jab of their bill seize their prey.

LITTLE BLUE HERON

Egretta caerulea, FAMILY ARDEIDAE (HERONS AND EGRETS)

Description: *Body* slate blue-gray; neck and head maroon purple; bill gray-blue with black tip; legs green-gray to green-yellow. *Juveniles* white, usually with dusky wing tips; young birds acquiring adult plumage often with mottled appearance. *Flies* with neck folded and legs extended.

Size: 25–30 inches tall; wing span to 3.4 ft.

Habitat: Freshwater swamps and brackish lagoons.

Nest: In small trees and bushes; built of sticks; generally in colonies; eggs 3–5, pale blue-green.

Diet: Mainly small fish; adults usually forage alone; juveniles tend to feed in groups.

Note: Unlike many other herons and egrets, the Little Blue Heron has no fancy plumes and thus was spared from 19th century plume hunting.

GREAT BLUE HERON

Ardea herodias, FAMILY ARDEIDAE (HERONS AND EGRETS)

Description: *Body* large, blue-gray; head white with black stripe over eye; bill pale or yellowish; legs long, green-yellow to brown-yellow. In southern Florida an all white form, "Great White Heron", differs from the Great Egret in being larger, with legs any color other than black. *Flies* with neck folded and legs extended.

Size: 39–54 inches; wing span to 5.8 ft.

Habitat: Lakes, ponds, rivers, coastal lagoons and marshes.

Nest: In colonies high in tall trees (on IRL spoil islands in Australian Pines, see page 11); built as large shallow platform of sticks; eggs 3–7, pale greenish-blue.

Diet: Larger fish, frogs, mice, snakes, small birds and insects.

Note: In late summer, young herons disperse widely and may be encountered at small ponds or even in backyard pools, wherever fish are available.

YELLOW-CROWNED NIGHT-HERON

Nyctanassa violacea, FAMILY ARDEIDAE (HERONS AND EGRETS)

Description: *Body* medium-size, slate-gray; head black; neck and underparts lighter gray; cheeks white; crown and plumes yellow to cream; bill black, stout; legs yellow or orange. *Juveniles* gray-brown, finely speckled with white above. *Flies* with neck folded and legs extended.

Size: 22–27 inches tall; wing span to 3.7 ft.

Habitat: Wooded swamps and coastal mangrove thickets; mainly nocturnal.

Nest: In trees, rarely on ground; built of sticks; singly or in small colonies, occasionally with other herons; eggs 3–5, blue-green.

Diet: Crushes fish and crabs with short, powerful bill.

Note: Increased and expanded its range northward in recent decades.

DOUBLE-CRESTED CORMORANT

Phalacrocorax auritus, FAMILY PHALACROCORACIDAE (CORMORANTS)

Description: *Body* black; throat pouch yellow-orange; neck long; bill long, hooked, top black, lower parts yellow; feet black; during breeding season adults have short tuft of feathers over each eye. *Juveniles* browner, whitish or light beige on chest, upper belly and neck. *Flies* with distinct crook in neck.

Size: 28–35 inches.

Habitat: Lakes, rivers, swamps, lagoons, estuaries and coastal bays.

Nest: In trees, on cliffs or rocky islands; built as bulky platform of sticks and seaweeds; often in colonies with Anhinga; eggs 3–5, chalky, pale blue-green.

Diet: Fish and crustaceans; use their wings to literally fly underwater, can swallow a surprisingly large fish.

Note: Despite years of persecution by fishermen (who viewed the Cormorant as a competitor), this species is currently increasing in numbers. Feathers not fully waterproof, birds often perch with wings outstretched to dry.

ANHINGA

Anhinga anhinga, FAMILY ANHINGIDAE (AHNINGAS)

Description: *Body* black with greenish gloss, shaped similar to Cormorant but with longer, more slender, S-shaped neck; eyes red; bill long, narrow, dagger-like, yellow to yellow-orange with dusky tip; tail long, fan-shaped. *Male's* plumage has greenish iridescence; upper surface of wings silver gray. *Female* with tawny-

brown head, neck and chest, sharply differentiated from black belly. *Flies* with neck extended and tail fanned.

Size: 34–36 inches; wing span to 4 ft.

Habitat: Freshwater tributaries of the IRL, swamps and mangrove areas, especially where there are large trees.

Nest: In trees; built as platform of sticks; often in colonies with Double-Crested Cormorants; eggs 3–5, chalky, blue to greenish white.

Diet: Fish.

Note: Also known as 'Snakebird' and 'Water Turkey'; often swims with body submerged and only head and long slender neck visible above water. Its long, dagger shaped, serrated bill is ideally suited for stabbing fish. Feathers not waterproof; birds often perch with wings outstretched to dry.

RED-SHOULDERED HAWK

Buteo lineatus subspecies *lineatus*, FAMILY ACCIPITRIDAE (HAWKS AND EAGLES)

Description: *Body* large, long-winged, with white barring on dark wings; shoulders rusty; underparts pale, barred with rust; tail with narrow white bands; in flight, shows translucent area near tip of wing, visible from below. *Juveniles* brownish above, cream-buff below, heavily streaked with dark brown.

Size: 16–24 inches tall; wing span to 3.3 ft.

Habitat: Swampy woods, bogs and estuaries.

Nest: High in trees; built as large mass of leaves and twigs; eggs 2–3, white with brown spots.

Diet: Snakes, frogs, insects and small mammals.

Note: Feeds by still-hunting from perches. Two subspecies, one (*elegans*) found in Baja, Mexico, and the other (*lineatus*) encountered in eastern Mexico, Texas, Mississippi, Louisiana and Florida.

OSPREY (FISH HAWK)

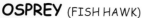

Pandion haliaetus, FAMILY ACCIPITRIDAE (HAWKS AND EAGLES)

Description: *Body* large, long-winged; dark brown above, white below; head white with dark brown line through eye and on sides of face; tail tipped white, upperside barred gray-brown and dark brown, underside barred dark and light gray.

Size: 21–24 inches tall; wing span to 6 ft.

Habitat: Lakes, rivers and estuaries.

Nest: In trees, on telephone poles, rock pinnacles or rarely flat ground; built as bulky mass of sticks, seaweeds and debris; eggs 2–4, white, pink or buff, blotched with brown.

Diet: Live fish. Ospreys search for fish by flying and hovering over water, when prey is sighted, dives steeply with talons outstretched and splashes into the water, quickly resurfaces and carries off the catch.

Note: Ospreys declined drastically because of pesticides during the 1950's and 1960's, but, since DDT pesticides were banned, have made a major comeback.

AMERICAN WHITE PELICAN

Pelecanus erythrorhynchos, FAMILY PELECANIDAE (PELICANS)

Description: *Body* huge, stocky, white; wing tips black; bill long, flat, orange-yellow, tip hooked; throat pouch huge; facial skin and feet orange; back of head with short yellowish crest during breeding season. *Flies* with head folded back onto shoulders.

Size: 55–70 inches tall; wing span to 9.5 ft.

Habitat: Shallow lakes, coastal lagoons and estuaries; generally in flocks, common in northern IRL during winter.

Nest: As low mound of earth and debris on marshy islands; in colonies; eggs 1–6, whitish. Breeds in more northern climates; winters in Florida.

Diet: Fish.

Note: White Pelican flocks cooperate in foraging for fish by surrounding schools, scooping both fish and water into their pouches. Because of pesticides, human disturbance and the draining of wetlands, this species is in decline.

BROWN PELICAN

Pelecanus occidentalis, FAMILY PELECANIDAE (PELICANS)

Description: *Body* large, stocky, dark brown to silver-gray; bill long, flat, grayish, tip hooked; throat pouch huge; head and neck white to yellow in adults, with dark brown mane during breeding season. *Juveniles* with dark brown head, whitish bellies. *Flies* with head folded back onto shoulders.

Size: 45–54 inches tall; wing span to 7.5 ft.

Habitat: Coastal beaches, estuaries, lagoons, waterfronts, pilings and rocky cliffs.

Nest: In mangrove trees; built of sticks, grass or debris; in colonies; eggs 2–3, chalky white.

Diet: Fish.

Note: The only non-white pelican in the world. These social birds fly in single file low over the water; on sighting prey they plunge with wings half folded, from heights of up to 50 ft., surfacing to drain water from their bills before swallowing the catch.

Common Mammals

BOTTLE-NOSED DOLPHIN

Tursiops truncates, FAMILY DELPHINIDAE (DOLPHIN)

Description: *Color* of individuals vary from albino to nearly black, generally light gray; dark blue-gray above; pink or white below; head and back often with dark cape. *Body* robust; forehead with obvious bump; beak short, well defined, broad; crosswise groove between forehead and snout; dorsal fin near center of back, prominent, broad-based, tip pointed.

Size: To 12 ft. long, smaller in the IRL.

Breeding: 1 young every 2–3 years; around 3 ft. long at birth.

Habitat: Estuaries, shallow bays, waterways and freshwater rivers.

Diet: Fish (especially mullet), squid, shrimp and crabs. Particularly adept at locating prey using echolocation (projecting sound waves and listening to the returning echo).

Note: Also known as the Bottle-Nosed Porpoise, Gray Porpoise, Common Porpoise and Black Porpoise. The name may be prefixed by Atlantic or Pacific. Known for riding ships' bow waves.

MANATEE

Trichechus manatus, FAMILY TRICHECHIDAE (MANATEE)

Description: *Body* massive, Walrus-like, nearly hairless, gray to black; tail broad, flattened, paddle-shaped; head broad; upper lip deeply cleft, with stiff bristles; front legs large, flipper-like; hindlegs absent.

Size: To 13 ft. long; maximum weight 3,500 lb.

Breeding: Mating season variable; 1 offspring produced every 2–3 years.

Habitat: Totally aquatic; shallow coastal waters, bays, rivers, estuaries and lakes.

Diet: Aquatic vegetation, particularly seagrasses and Water Hyacinth.

Note: Manatees are primarily nocturnal, usually slow moving, moderately social and congregate in warm water in winter. They can remain submerged for up to 24 minutes, but about 4 minutes is normal. Adults consume 60 to 100 pounds of vegetation per day. Classified as endangered throughout its USA range. Human population growth has altered Manatee habitats by development, power plants, boating and other disturbances.

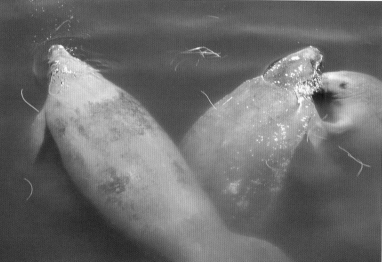

COMMON RACCOON

Procyon lotor, FAMILY PROCYONIDAE

Description: *Body* gray-brown or orange-brown mixed with black above; grayish below; face has black mask outlined in white; tail bushy, with 4–6 alternating black and brown or brownish-gray rings.

Size: 24–37 inches long; to 16 inches tall; maximum weight 48 lb.

Habitat: Various wooded and wetland habitats; common on the banks of the Indian River Lagoon, especially in impoundment areas.

Diet: Omnivorous; nuts, berries, grubs, grasshoppers, crickets, mice, other small mammals, bird eggs, crabs, frogs, worms, fish, clams, turtles and turtle eggs.

Note: Nocturnal and solitary except when breeding or caring for its young. An accomplished climber.

NORTHERN RIVER OTTER

Lontra canadensis, FAMILY MUSTELIDAE (WEASEL)

Description: *Body* elongated, broad, dark brown above (black when wet); belly paler; throat generally silver gray; head flattened; ears and eyes small; whiskers whitish; tail long, thick at base, tapering to point; feet webbed.

Size: 35–52 inches long; 11–20 inches tall; weight 11–30 lb.

Habitat: Rivers, canals, ponds, lakes, estuaries and mangroves, generally in IRL wooded impoundment channels.

Diet: Fish, captured in quick sideways snap, also small mammals (mangrove rats), as well as aquatic invertebrates.

Note: Unless disturbed by humans, this entertaining animal is generally active during the day. Well adapted to the aquatic environment with its streamlined body, sturdy rudder-like tail and unique ear and nostril valves that keep out water. Known for performing acrobatics both on land (playfully sliding and tumbling) and in the water (flexible, graceful and powerful swimmer). Otters can remain submerged for several minutes, dive to 55 ft. and swim as far as 0.25 mile underwater. Many anglers accuse the Northern River Otter of depleting gamefish stocks. They consume very few gamefish, preferring slower moving or schooling baitfish that are easier prey. The Northern River Otter's fur is highly prized for its durability and beauty. In the past, excessive trapping diminished otter populations and, more recently, pollution has taken a toll.

WIDGEON GRASS

Ruppia maritima, FAMILY POTAMOGETONACEAE

Description: *Plants* coarse, firm, with narrow flattened leaves, grass green; flowers and fruits small but conspicuous. *Leaves* to 8 inches long, arising directly from runner joint, stalk absent, each cluster of 2–4 leaves. *Runners* thin, branching common, often extending vertically to appear as stalk, especially during flowering. *Roots* one per joint, generally unbranched.

Size: To 24 inches high, covering small to large areas.

Habitat: Common, in brackish waters of bays and estuaries, widely distributed; forming dense stands in muddy sediments.

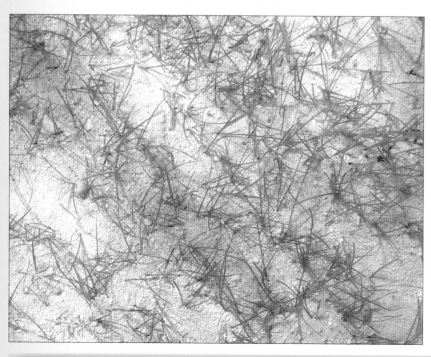

Note: One of the few seagrasses that lives in both saltwater and freshwater environments. Widgeon Grass is one of the IRL's most commonly observed seagrasses because it often grows above the surface in very shallow water to form marsh-like zones. It is a waterfowl magnet, particularly in the 27,000 acres of northern impoundments isolated from the IRL's saline waters.

SHOAL GRASS

Halodule wrightii, FAMILY CYMODOCEACEAE

Description: *Plants* coarse, grass green, stiff but pliable, grass-like; root system relatively weak; flowers and fruits small, inconspicuous. *Leaves* to 0.1 inches wide, 8 inches long, narrowed at base, one cluster per joint; center vein conspicuous; parallel marginal veins present but not as conspicuous as center vein; leaf tip having three teeth; central tooth 1–10 times longer than lateral teeth. *Runners* extensive, creeping. *Roots* 1–4 per joint.

Size: To 10 inches high, forming small to large patches.

Habitat: Common, on sandy, soft, muddy bottoms.

Note: Shoal Grass, along with Manatee Grass, dominates the northern IRL. It is one of the first plants to re-seed after a severe boat grounding and, therefore, can be an indicator of fairly recent disturbance. Extremely well adapted to shallow shoals, *Halodule* is found from the upper reaches of the Mosquito Lagoon southward in just several inches of water to as deep as 6 ft.

PADDLE GRASS

Halophila decipiens, FAMILY HYDROCHARITACEAE

Description: *Plants* delicate, small, in leafy patches, bright green; flowers and fruits small, inconspicuous. *Leaves* oval, paddle-shaped, 0.1-0.3 inches wide, to 1 inch long, one pair per node (joint); margin with extremely fine teeth; marginal veins splitting from central vein at leaf base, paralleling margin, meeting central vein again just below leaf tip; cross veins faint, 6–9 pairs. *Runners* thin, extensive. *Roots* one per node opposite leaf pair.

Size: To 1 inch high, small to large patches.

Habitat: Common, in calm waters on soft sand or fine sedimentary bottoms.

Note: Paddle Grass and its close relatives—Star and Johnson's Seagrasses—are sparsely distributed, but indicators of good habitat quality. Paddle Grass tolerates the lowest light of all of the IRL's seagrasses where it occurs as patchy colonies in clear or stained waters from Sebastian southward.

STAR GRASS

Halophila engelmanni, FAMILY HYDROCHARITACEAE

Description: *Plants* delicate, in leafy patches, bright green; flowers and fruits small, inconspicuous. *Stalk* slender, to 2 inches long, one per joint. *Leaves* oval, to 0.2 inches wide, 1.2 inches long, in 2–4 close set pairs (appearing in rings) at tip of stalk; tip blunt, occasionally with spine; base wedge-shaped; margin finely toothed; marginal veins splitting from central vein at leaf base, paralleling margin, meeting central vein again just below leaf apex; cross veins faint, 6–8 pairs. *Runners* thin. *Roots* one per joint, opposite upright stalk, soon covered by fine rootlets.

Size: To 14 inches high, small to large patches.

Habitat: Uncommon, but widely distributed; in calm waters on soft sand of fine sediment bottoms.

Note: This subtropical plant is large enough to contribute habitat structure from Cape Canaveral southward in depths to 6 ft. In the IRL, Star Grass reaches its peak abundance near Merritt Island in the northern expanse of the Indian River.

JOHNSON'S SEAGRASS

Halophila johnsonii, FAMILY HYDROCHARITACEAE

Description: *Plants* delicate, small, in leafy patches, bright green; flowers and fruits small, inconspicuous. *Stems* slender, to 0.8 inches long. *Leaves* oval, to 1.5 inches wide, 1 inch long, one pair per joint; margin smooth, without teeth; marginal veins splitting from central vein at leaf base, paralleling margin, meeting central vein again just below leaf tip; cross veins faint, 5–10 offset pairs. *Runners* extensive. *Roots* thin, one per joint opposite leaf pair; rootlets colorless.

Size: To 2 inches high, small to large patches.

Habitat: Uncommon, in calm waters on soft sand or fine sedimentary bottoms; commonly occurring in the Indian River Lagoon to 5 ft. deep.

Note: Found nowhere in the world but along the southeast coast of Florida between Melbourne and Key Biscayne, its primary habitat is the Indian River Lagoon. It is usually found in a few inches to 5 ft. of water. A fragile plant, Johnson's Seagrass is susceptible to dredge-and-fill development and increased nutrients from agricultural runoff and has been given Threatened Species status.

SEAWEEDS
INDICATORS OF WATER QUALITY

RED ALGAE (Rhodophyta)

HYPNEA FAMILY HYPNEACEAE

Description: *Plants* wiry, upright or in tangled mats, brown-red; branching in any direction. *Branches* thin, cylindrical. *Branchlets* spine-, spur- or tendril-like, numerous, to 0.1 inch long, occasionally longer; tips tapering, pointed. *Holdfast* inconspicuous, pad-like, most commonly attached to seagrasses by ensnaring tendrils.

Size: To 3 inches high.

Habitat: Common, on rocks, seagrasses or tangled on larger seaweeds; to 15 ft. in the IRL.

Note: An indicator of healthy conditions. Seaweeds, such as *Hypnea* and the others depicted below, grow much deeper than seagrasses in the IRL. Seaweeds, thereby, also create additional habitat, food and oxygen, while simultaneously stripping excess water column nutrients that might lead to harmful light-robbing phytoplankton blooms.

GRACILARIA FAMILY GRACILARIACEAE

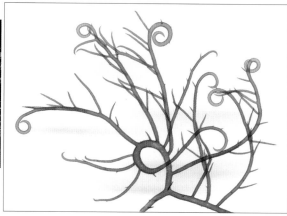

Description: *Plants* brittle to leathery, erect or creeping with erect tips, bright red, brownish red to greenish red; branching irregular, occasionally dichotomous at tips. *Branches* cylindrical to slightly compressed (oval in cross section), often slightly pinched at base of branch; tips bluntly rounded or pointed. *Holdfasts* small, disc-like.

Size: To 6 inches high, forming small to large clumps, in the IRL to 12 ft. deep.

Habitat: Conspicuous over large areas, growing attached to rubble, drifting free or tangled in seagrass beds.

Note: Indicator of very healthy conditions in the IRL, forming significant 3-dimensional structure used for shelter and forage by invertebrates and small fish. All of the IRL species of *Gracilaria* are potentially valuable for their agar content. Some can be eaten in fish or meat dishes or added to chicken stew causing it to thicken and gelatinize upon cooling. In the Caribbean, *Gracilaria* is made into a "Sea Moss" drink reported to be an aphrodisiac.

GREEN ALGAE (Chlorophyta)

CAULERPA FAMILY CAULERPACEAE

Description: *Uprights* bearing small, often crowded, bead-like, feather-like or blade-like branchlets, grass-green; unbranched or branched. *Branchlets* spherical, oval, club-shaped, needle-like or in fine branching whorls. *Runners* creeping, often branched.

PENICILLUS FAMILY UDOTEACEAE

Description: *Plants* stiff, calcified, shaving brush-like, dull blue-green. *Cap* smoothly rounded, spherical to oblong, occasionally flat-topped, to 2.5 inches in diameter. *Rhizoidal mass* bulb-like.

Size: To 7 inches high.

Habitat: In calm lagoons and bays, on mud or sand bottoms, this 'rooted' form of seaweed is often intermixed with healthy IRL seagrasses or among mangrove prop roots; to 6 ft. deep.

Note: Indicator of healthy grass flat conditions from Fort Pierce Inlet southward.

HALIMEDA FAMILY HALIMEDACEAE

Description: *Plants* erect, compact, often as dense clumps, dark green to yellow-tinged light green; two or three branches arising from single segment, sparse, occasionally denser near base. *Segments* large, calcified, with or without ribs, flat, disc-like, oval to wedge-shaped. *Joints* flexible, not calcified. *Stalk* is basal segment, cylindrical to fan-shaped, absent in some species. *Holdfast* small and conspicuous when growing on rock, large fibrous 'rootlets' bind sediments when growing in sand or mud.

Size: To 9 inches high.

Habitat: Anchored ('rooted') by small bulb-like holdfast in sediments among seagrasses, in protected lagoons or mangrove communities, some species are attached to rocks, pebbles or other hard substrates; to 7 ft. deep.

Note: Indicator of very healthy grass flat conditions, mainly from St. Lucie Inlet southward.

ENTEROMORPHA ['*Enteromorpha*' means intestine-shaped]

FAMILY ULVACEAE

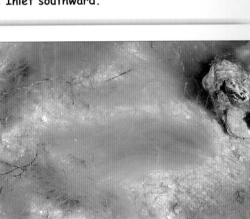

Description: *Plants* vary considerably from species to species, forming soft slick turfs, tufts, blades or long flowing masses; some species short, others longer, bright yellow-green to dull green; branching variable, from unbranched to irregularly branched. *Holdfast* pad of tightly knit rhizoids.

Size: To 2 ft. high.

Habitat: In wide range of habitats from mangrove and reef ecosystems to brackish waters of estuaries to fresh-

water seeps, on sandy shores, intertidal mud flats, mangrove prop roots, ropes or other solid objects in calm water, often associated with high nutrient areas (e.g., bird islands); shallow intertidal in IRL.

Note: Indicator of very high nutrient enrichment (bird rookery islands, groundwater septic tank seeps, pollution) or recently disturbed substrates.

Size: To 6 inches high.

Habitat: Most species of *Caulerpa* form intertwined mats tightly adhering to rocks or creeping over sand or mud, in moderately heavy surf areas or in calm lagoons and bays; intertidal to 15 ft. deep in the IRL.

Note: The native species depicted are indicators of moderately healthy conditions from Melbourne southward.

59

BROWN ALGAE (Phaeophyta)

HINCKSIA

FAMILY SPHACELARIACEAE

Description: *Plants* as dense finely filamentous tufts, medium to dark brown; branching irregular, abundant. *Filaments* straight, cylindrical, fine. *Runners* fibrous.

Size: To 1 inch high as small tufts, to 3 ft. long when flowing in currents.

Habitat: Mostly inconspicuous, at times (mainly winter months) can become a nuisance, on rock and other hard substrates, growing on oysters, seagrasses and coarse algae; intertidal IRL to 9 ft. deep.

Note: Indicator of overly enriched wintertime waters—a weedy nuisance alga.

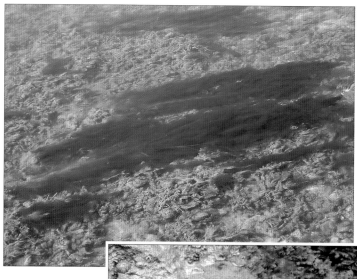

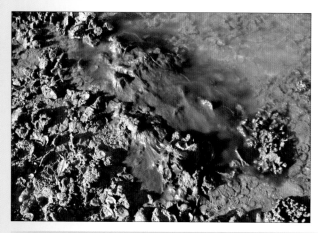

BLUE-GREEN ALGAE (Cyanobacteria)

LYNGBYA

FAMILY OSCILLATORIACEAE

Description: *Plants* filamentous, forming tangled masses, brown-green, yellow-green, black-green to black-purple. *Filaments* long, straight or curved, rarely coiled.

Size: To 20 inches long.

Habitat: Common mainly in summer; forming large mats in calm waters or unattached as free floating, black, hair-like mats; IRL intertidal to 6 ft. deep.

Note: Indicator of detrimentally unhealthy conditions. Produces compounds that can be toxic to fish, plants and invertebrates. Also, drifting mats are poisonous to mammals; causing swimmer's itch, a skin irritation that beach goers and divers commonly experience. Related species produce the universally present slippery black layer on boat ramps.

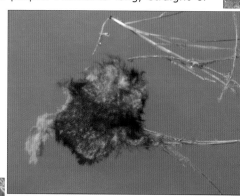

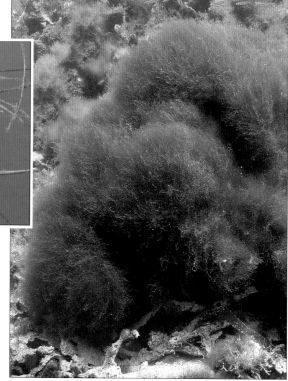

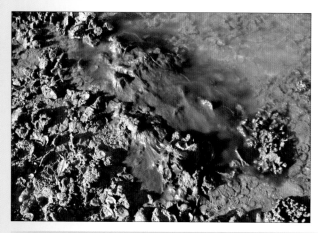

TREES AND MARSH PLANTS

AUSTRALIAN PINE (BEEFWOOD, IRONWOOD, SHE-OAK, HORESTAIL TREE, CASUARINA)

Casuarina equisetifolia, FAMILY CASUARINACEAE

Description: Evergreen; trunk generally single. *Branchlets* resembling pine needles, dark green, to 5 inches long; shed yearly. *Bark* red-brown to gray, rough, peeling. *Leaves* tiny, scale-like, encircling (whorled) twig at joints. *Roots* with nodules having symbiotic nitrogen-fixing bacteria allowing tree to thrive in nutrient poor soils.

Size: To 150 ft. high; trunk to 3 ft. in diameter.

Habitat: Introduced from Australia, *Casuarina* is an aggressive early successional species and is salt tolerant. Commonly found on spoil islands and disturbed shorelines of the Indian River Lagoon, often outcompeting and displacing native species.

Reproduction: *Flowers* inconspicuous. *Fruits* clustered, small, cone-like, brown, spherical.

Importance: Australian Pine has rapid growth, forms dense shade and accumulates thick litter. It is a soil stabilizer and helps to control erosion along banks and on spoil islands; numerous birds nest in *Casuarina* (p. 11).

Note: Although superficially resembling a pine, the Australian Pine is not related to pines. Often confused with the similar and common *Casuarina glauca* which has 8–10 inch pine needle-like branchlets, as well as abundant root suckers (new plants arising from roots, not present at base of *C. equisetifolia*).

RED MANGROVE

Rhizophora mangle, FAMILY RHIZOPHORACEAE

Description: Small shrub to large tree; growing in thickets with many tangled arched prop roots. *Leaves* thick, leathery, oval, shiny, dark green above, lighter yellow-green below; tip pointed; base tapering. *Bark* of mature trees smooth. *Prop roots* (also known as stilt or aerial roots) descending from trunk, branches and other anchored prop roots; specialized pores provide extra oxygen as an adaptation to muddy conditions.

Size: May exceed 100 ft. high; trunk to 3 ft. in diameter.

Habitat: On shallow muddy coastlines in water up to 3 ft. deep; can tolerate salinities ranging from freshwater to hypersalinity; able to withstand occasional severe storms, thereby protecting coastlines from erosion. In IRL, south of Cape Canaveral.

Reproduction: *Seeds* germinate on tree and produce thin pendulous plantlets up to a foot long before dropping; plantlets can survive in seawater for a year or on dry land for weeks. Only mangrove that can germinate below low tide level.

Importance: As nursery grounds; the copious organic debris produced by shed leaves and branches provide food; the submerged prop roots are essential habitat for immature forms of many marine organisms including crabs, lobsters, baitfishes and snappers (see photo, p. 5). This species and the other mangroves can produce enduring shorelines and ever-enlarging islands by accumulation of organic matter (leaf and twig debris) that can form mangrove peat deposits up to 25 ft. thick and 5,000 years old.

BLACK MANGROVE

Avicennia germinans, FAMILY VERBENACEAE

Description: Small shrub to large tree with scaly bark. *Leaves* lance-shaped, yellow-green above, gray-green below; margins smooth; tips gently tapering to point; base gently tapering. *Roots* send up gnarled pencil-sized air seeking roots that have numerous specialized pores to provide extra aeration under oxygen depleted conditions.

Size: To 65 ft. high; trunk to 3 ft. in diameter.

Habitat: In salty, silty, saturated soils along coastal areas at high water levels; can tolerate salinities from freshwater to hypersalinity; dies if air-roots are submerged by prolonged flooding.

Reproduction: *Seeds* germinate on tree and form tiny seedlings or plantlets. *Seedlings* can survive floating in seawater for over four months and longer in freshwater.

Importance: As a soil and shoreline stabilizer; promotes deposition of organic sediments that enter the decomposer food chain or contribute to mangrove peat formation.

WHITE MANGROVE

Laguncularia racemosa, FAMILY COMBRETACEAE

Description: Small shrub to large tree, often with multiple trunks; in saturated soil, a basal cone of tightly interlaced roots often develops. *Leaves* leathery, elliptical, opposite; surface with tiny white dots (pits); margins smooth; tip blunt or indented; two glands present on stalk at base of leaf. *Bark* of mature trees shaggy, rough, deeply grooved. *Roots* often send up stumpy thumb sized air seeking roots (most remain below soil level, rarely exposed) that have many specialized pores to provide extra aeration for the plant under otherwise oxygen depleted conditions.

Size: To 50 ft. high; trunk to 30 inches in diameter.

Habitat: In salty silty saturated soils at highest high water levels; dies if roots are submerged by prolonged flooding. In IRL, south of Cape Canaveral.

Reproduction: *Seeds* germinate on tree and form tiny seedlings or plantlets. *Fruit* flattened oval, less than 1 inch long, ribbed. *Seedlings* germinate within fruit while still on tree; can survive floating in seawater for up to one month (lose some vigor after 8 days); must be stranded above tidal influence for survival.

Importance: As soil stabilizer and controlling erosion along banks, organic debris fuels decomposer link of food chain and results in mangrove peat formation.

BUTTONWOOD (BUTTON MANGROVE)

Conocarpus erectus, FAMILY COMBRETACEAE (WHITE MANGROVE)

Description: Evergreen, spreading shrub to low-branching tree; crown rounded, narrow; thicket-forming with multiple trunks. *Leaves* alternate, 4 inches long, elliptical to lance-shaped; two glands present on stalk at base of leaf, lower surface with minute tissue pockets where major veins join midrib (center vein). *Bark* gray to dark brown, rough, ridged.

Size: To 30 ft. tall.

Habitat: In more open areas (does not like dense shade) on landward fringe of mangrove communities.

Reproduction: *Flowers* small, greenish, in tiny dense egg shaped heads ("buttons"); bloom year-round. *Fruit* cone-like, reddish-green, small, in 1 inch clusters, shatters when fruit is ripe.

Importance: In early Florida's past, an important source of charcoal.

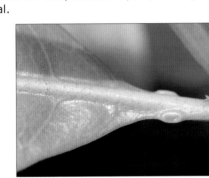

BRAZILIAN PEPPER (FLORIDA HOLLY, BRAZILIAN PEPPERTREE)

Schinus terebinthifolius, FAMILY ANACARDIACEAE (CASHEW)

Description: Evergreen shrub to small tree; trunk generally multi-stemmed; crown dense, uneven. *Bark* smooth, gray-brown. *Branches* arched, tangled. *Leaves* to 6 inches long, alternately compound with 3–11 leaflets. *Leaflets* to 2 inches long, oval with gently pointed tip; upper surface dark green; veins lighter; margins toothed; exude turpentine odor when crushed.

Size: To 43 ft. high; trunk to 2 ft. in diameter.

Habitat: Edges of spoil islands, impoundment dikes, hammocks, mangrove swamps, pinelands, disturbed areas.

Reproduction: *Flowers* tiny, white, in short-branched clusters. *Fruit* bright red, spherical, berry-like.

Importance: Introduced; forms dense thickets that shade out and replace native vegetation.

Note: Warning—the resinous sap can cause skin irritation.

SALT MARSH CORD GRASS (SALTWATER CORD GRASS, SPARTINA)

Spartina alterniflora, FAMILY POACEAE (GRASSES)

Description: Herbaceous (not woody). *Stems* cylindrical, jointed, hollow between joints. *Leaves* linear, flat, alternate (oriented on opposite sides), in 2 opposite rows on stem, bases forming sheath around stem.

Habitat: Open brackish areas and tidal flats; extensive colonies cover large lagoon or spoil island areas, often forcing out other species (see also p. 9).

Reproduction: *Flowers* beige, very small, scale-like, arranged on spikelet. *Spikelets* upright, to 6 inches long. *Fruit* as tiny grains.

Importance: Plays a major role in stabilizing sediments to slow erosion, produces marine compost and shelters juvenile fishes and invertebrates to sustain IRL fisheries.

Note: Burrowing crabs are a major component of the Cord Grass habitat, not only providing food for fish and other animals, but also in stimulating grass growth. If Fiddler Crabs are removed experimentally, the productivity (growth) of Cord Grass is cut in half.

AMERICAN GLASSWORT (SAMPHIRE)

Salicornia virginica, FAMILY CHENOPODIACEAE (GOOSEFOOT)

Description: Herbaceous (not woody), to 7 inches tall, fleshy above, wiry below, tangled, creeping, seldom reaching bush stature. *Stems* cylindrical, jointed, 4–24 inches long; outer parts fleshy, succulent, crisp. *Leaves* inconspicuous, scale-like, bright green, surrounding stalk; stem appears leafless.

Habitat: Open, wet, brackish areas and tidal flats; extensive colonies often force out other species.

Reproduction: *Flowers* green, minute, embedded in upper joints. *Fruiting spike* to 2 inches long. *Seeds* inconspicuous, tiny, hairy.

Importance: Plays a major role in protecting against erosion, especially in the northern IRL; does not survive in freshwater filled impoundments.

SALTWORT (BEACHWORT, PICKLEWEED)

Batis maritima, FAMILY BATACEAE

Description: Herbaceous (not woody), to 3 ft. tall, large masses often found creeping over mangrove air roots; in the northern Lagoon, forming taller shrubs; root system often extensive. *Stems* cylindrical, brittle. *Leaves* fleshy, smooth, pale to bright green, opposite, to 1 inch long, narrowly club-shaped, curved.

Habitat: Wet, brackish areas, tidal flats and salt marshes; extensive colonies often force out other species.

Reproduction: *Flowers* minute, greenish white, in short spikes. *Fruit* cone-like, yellow, fleshy, to 0.8 inches long.

Importance: Plays a major role in protecting against erosion; replaces Cord Grass marshes in northern IRL, particularly on Mosquito Lagoon islands.

Aerial Photographs from Jupiter Inlet to Ponce de Leon Inlet

The following 51 seamless color images are indexed (page numbered) with an equal number of locator frames drawn on maps found within both front and back inside covers (end plates). These images provide a unique continuous overview of the entire IRL, extending approximately 156 miles northward from Jupiter Inlet and terminating at Ponce de Leon Inlet. We feel that it would be misleading to label the aerial photographs with species-specific angling 'hot spots', because these change seasonally, daily and even hourly. Too much lettering also would obscure the spectacular resolution and habitat detail revealed in the uncluttered photographs. Instead, we have designated only key landmarks, boat ramps (triangles), compass headings, size scales and GPS locations for orientation. Once you practice ground-truthing several images from familiar IRL areas, you will become able to recognize mangroves, salt marshes, seagrass beds, impoundment dikes, spoil islands, shoals, channels, holes and the many obscure byways. Ample space is provided to accommodate your own personal notes and records, which will have far more relevance as you continue to explore the IRL's hidden waterways and back country. Please use these images only for general information and not for navigation. Obtain updated NOAA and USCG navigational charts and enjoy safe boating.

IRL ANGLING OVERVIEW

We have provided the following summary overview (in very broad brush strokes) giving highlights of the angling opportunities to be found in the regions photographed. In the Indian River Lagoon, good fishing is usually available almost anywhere, and throughout the year as well. Birding and photography by boat are also rewarding most of the year, but reach peaks when the winter shorebird and waterfowl migrations occur. Fishing, in general, is usually best when the larger fish move in to feed during the spring and fall runs of baitfish, particularly the September through October Silver Mullet run.

With the Indian River Lagoon beginning as far south as Jupiter Inlet, it is not surprising that the fisheries of the Palm and Treasure Coasts differ markedly from those of the Space Coast region to the north. For example, the diversity of catchable fish is substantially higher in the southern section of the IRL. Wide ranging anglers also soon realize that Redfish and Black Drum become much more numerous and constitute larger size classes toward the northern IRL. The tradeoff is that Snook and Tarpon more than compensate for the difference; being much more abundant, while averaging larger in size, toward the south.

From Jupiter Inlet to St. Lucie Inlet, opportunities for undisturbed angling are less than optimal. These narrow waters are continuously disturbed by fast moving large watercraft, except during hours of darkness. That said, the IRL's healthiest seagrass beds and mangrove forests occur between Jupiter Inlet and Hobe Sound; where, as in the cases of St. Lucie and Fort Pierce Inlets, transient schools of Bonefish and Permit move in to feed during the summer season. Those with a boat can consistently catch Snook from under marina and private docks at night, providing a mainstay fishery and job security for area guides much of the year. The wider areas in this stretch (such as Pecks Lake) are loaded with young trout, jacks and, especially, schooling Ladyfish, offering action for fly fishers and light tackle anglers. The Snook are just as abundant at Jupiter Inlet as in any of the other inlets, with the Loxahatchee River providing exceptional Snook opportunities year round, in addition to substantial Bluefish runs during the winter months.

Within the St. Lucie Inlet proper, big jacks and summertime Tarpon are common along with 20 pound Snook. Snook of this size, or larger, are abundant all the way from St. Lucie to Sebastian Inlet. At dawn and dusk, lunker Snook in the south-central region of the IRL are frequently found on the shallow grass flats that adjoin mangroves ambushing mullet, sardines, herring or anchovies and offer incredible action, particularly for fly rodders. Along with the Snook will be gator trout, some in the double digit weight categories. Big Tarpon and Crevalle Jack are also frequently taken in these waters. A boat is definitely an asset for reaching the majority of the 'blue ribbon' flats, but some are accessible to wade fishers.

Fort Pierce Inlet is not quite as heavily fished as other inlets and offers excellent opportunities for shore and bank casters. Large Snook, jacks, some Redfish, Spanish Mackerel and Tarpon can be taken in summer. In addition, smaller panfish like snapper, Florida Pompano and Sheepshead are popular, while flounder, Bluefish and more mackerel show up during the winter months. The quarter-mile-diameter Turning Basin at the west end of Fort Pierce Inlet is unique in that it is quite deep (30 feet), loaded with nearby structure, well lighted and ripped by strong tidal currents. This location is home to jacks, snapper, grouper and schools of Bluefish, with Snook attracting a dedicated following of cold-season nighttime anglers.

Wade fishing is among the best approaches in the section of the Indian River Lagoon between Fort Pierce Inlet and Sebastian Inlet. Highway US1 parallels the western side of the lagoon and State Road A1A provides access to the eastern side. Extensive wadable grass flats support Snook, Seatrout, flounder, Redfish, baby Tarpon and a wealth of other species. Private docks also are excellent sites for a variety of gamefish. The Sebastian Inlet is allegedly the best Snook fishery in Florida. Angling access areas at the inlet are popular, with droves of fishermen casting or still fishing using conventional tackle. With a boat, you can reach flats not available to wade fishers, as well as the numerous spoil islands along the Intracoastal Waterway and the Tarpon and Snook filled waters of the Sebastian River. The Sebastian River's US1 and railroad bridges are excellent for summer Sheepshead, Snook, Seatrout and Redfish, while the upper South Fork and North Fork provide world class spring and summer Tarpon action.

Ocean access into the IRL's northernmost Mosquito Lagoon is from Ponce de Leon Inlet, and into the northern Banana River via Port Canaveral to the south (by a more restricted lock system). The Space Coast region of the IRL provides excellent opportunities for all types of angling, reputedly ranking among the finest of shallow-water, spot-and-stalk, Redfish fisheries on the planet. The area reportedly claims 16 current fly tackle world records among half a dozen different species of fish. Unlike most other IRL locales, mature Redfish do not emigrate to offshore breeding grounds from this section of the Indian River Lagoon (including the northern Indian River, Banana River and the Mosquito Lagoon). Also, the mangrove and seagrass habitats favored by Spotted Seatrout and Snook to the south give way to the marsh/mud systems favored by Redfish in the north. This affords a unique opportunity to pursue tremendous schools of giant Redfish, averaging better than 20 pounds each. In this region of the IRL, it is possible to sight cast to gigantic Redfish and Black Drum tailing in three feet of water! Even more-abundant, populations of smaller fish are approachable by wade fishers on the shallow flats. In addition to wade fishing, canoeing, kayaking or power boating will provide ample access to such targets as Black Drum, Spotted Seatrout, Tarpon, Snook and a wealth of other species.

The southern section of the Banana River (from Dragon Point to State Route 520) is overdeveloped and is not reputed to be a very productive area; whereas, the middle section (SR 520 to SR 528) is good for summertime Tarpon and Snook, as well as wintertime Redfish and Spotted Seatrout in the deeper pockets. The northern section of the Banana River is an extremely important Marine Sanctuary, with car-top boat or wading access only (no motorized watercraft permitted). The best place to launch a rowboat, kayak or canoe is just before the USAF-NASA Gate along the State Route 401 shoreline. Be aware that following the assault of 11 Sept. 2001, the eastside from State Route 528 to the NASA Causeway has been placed off-limits. This part of the Banana River provides some of the east coast's most awesome flats angling for those energetic enough to forego their reliance on a powerboat. Remember, motorized vessels are not permitted in the Banana River north of the high-power lines to the north of Route 528 at Port Canaveral.

The whole Mosquito Lagoon provides an outstanding year-round shallow water fishery for Redfish, Black Drum and Spotted Seatrout, in addition to summer Snook and Tarpon. The abundant margins of Glasswort/Saltwort marshes, robust Shoal Grass beds, mud flats, oyster reefs and sandbars are extremely productive. The preferred season for running the Mosquito Lagoon back country is during September through October. At this time of year, the comfort levels are highest and fishing opportunities are greatest. Also, the overall water levels in the whole IRL are about one foot higher on average than in January, mainly because of seawater heating/expansion. Even during this time, the Mosquito Lagoon east of the ICW can be quite hazardous to run without local knowledge, due to the abundance and extent of shallow flats and massive oyster bars. Poling and wading are necessary to navigate in these waters. In this regard, a new genre of high-tech carbon-fiber tunnel boats, capable of running in as little as four inches of water, has been specifically developed to deal with this type of shallow fishery.

US1

707

26°57.14'N
80°04.73'W

LOXAHATCHEE RIVER

INTRACOASTAL WATERWAY

JUPITER INLET

0.5 mile

W S N E

Field Records

_____
_____
_____
_____
_____
_____
_____

INTRACOASTAL WATERWAY

JUPITER SOUND

US1

707

0.5 mile

Field Records

US1

HELLS
GATE

26°58.54'N
80°05.09'W

INTRACOASTAL WATERWAY

707

W

S

E

Field Records

US1

CONCH
BAR

INTRACOASTAL WATERWAY

707

0.5 mile

Field Records

_____
_____
_____
_____
_____
_____
_____
_____

US1

INTRACOASTAL WATERWAY

HOBE SOUND

27°00.48'N
80°05.71'W

707

Field Records

INTRACOASTAL WATERWAY

A1A

Bascule Bridge

27°03.86'N
80°07.33'W

SOUTH JUPIT

707

0.5 mile

Field Records

_____

_____

_____

_____

_____

_____

_____

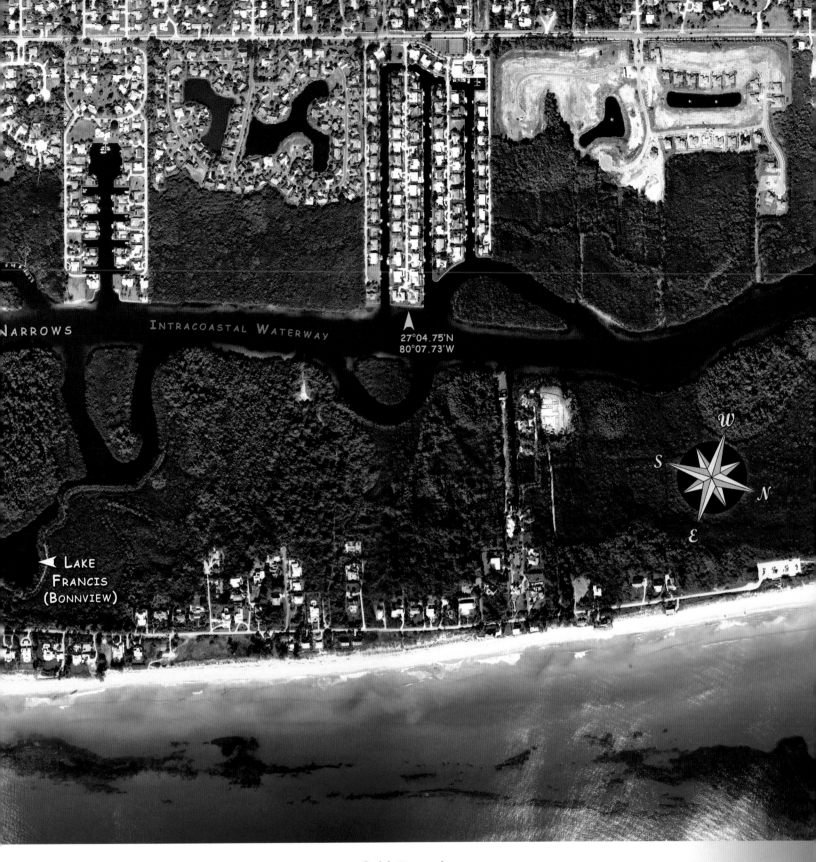

NARROWS   INTRACOASTAL WATERWAY

27°04.75'N
80°07.73'W

LAKE
FRANCIS
(BONNVIEW)

W
S
N
E

Field Records

_____

_____

_____

_____

_____

_____

_____

_____

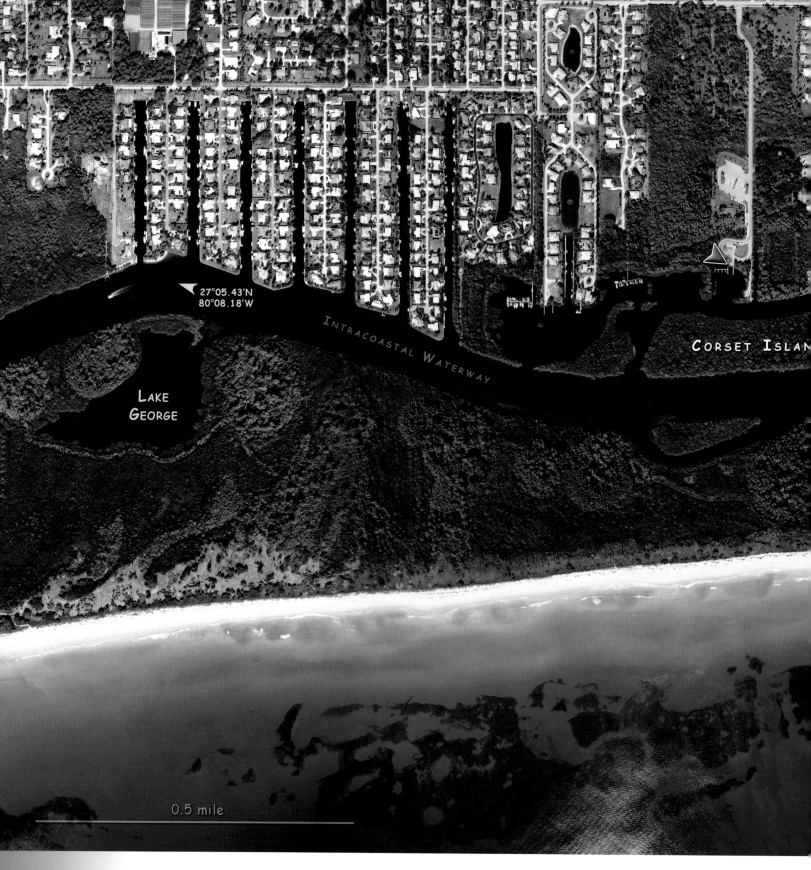

27°05.43'N
80°08.18'W

INTRACOASTAL WATERWAY

CORSET ISLAN

LAKE
GEORGE

0.5 mile

Field Records

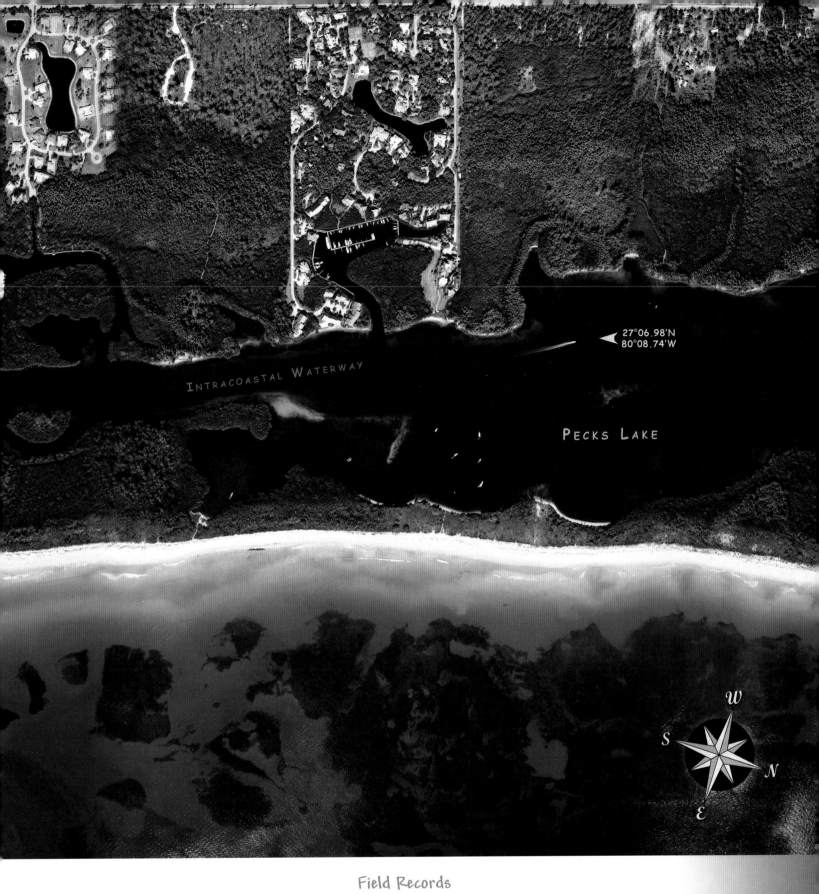

27°06.98'N
80°08.74'W

INTRACOASTAL WATERWAY

PECKS LAKE

Field Records

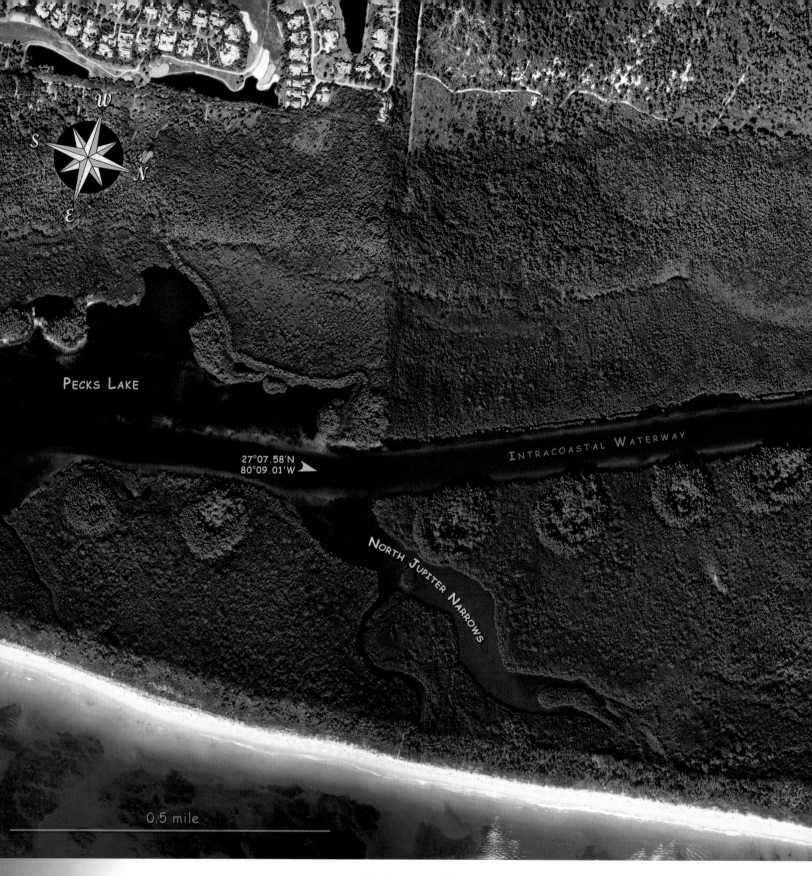

PECKS LAKE

27°07.58'N
80°09.01'W ➤

INTRACOASTAL WATERWAY

NORTH JUPITER NARROWS

0.5 mile

Field Records

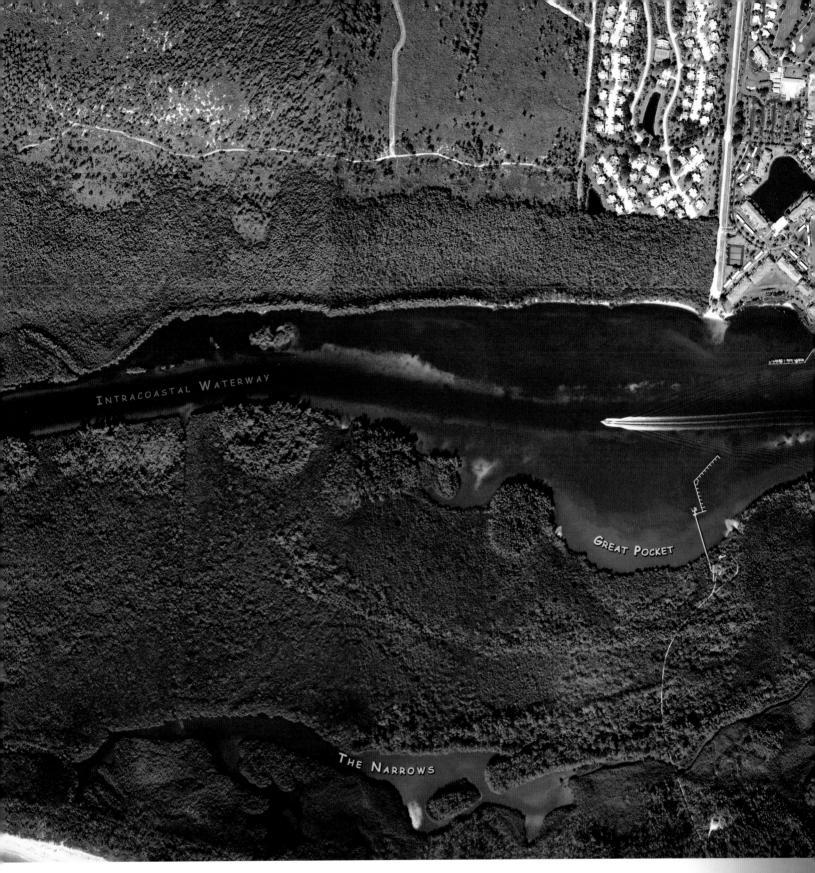

INTRACOASTAL WATERWAY

GREAT POCKET

THE NARROWS

Field Records

MANATEE POCKET

STUART

WILLOUGHBY CREEK

HOOKER COVE

27°09.80'N
80°11.50'W

ST. LUCI

SEWALL'S POINT

ROCKY
POINT

INTRACOASTAL WATERWAY

BIRD
ISLAND

HORSESHOE
POINT

LONG
POINT

27°09.87'N
80°10.10'W

HOLE IN
THE WALL

SAILFISH
COVE

SOUTH POINT

ST. LUCIE INLET

SAILFISH POINT

BESSIE
COVE

DETACHED
JETTY

NORTH JETTY

Field Records

_____
_____
_____
_____
_____
_____
_____
_____

RIVER

A1A

HOGGS COVE

RACES POINT

INTRACOASTAL WATERWAY

27°12.42'N
80°11.50'W

Stuart Causeway

INDIAN RIVER

JOES POINT
27°14.39'N
80°11.83'W

BAKER POINT

JOES COVE

A1A

1 mile

Field Records

JENSEN BEACH

707

JENSEN BEACH

INTRACOASTAL WATERWAY

Jensen Beach Causeway

27°15.20'N
80°13.13'W

732

A1A

1 mile

Field Records

707

INTRACOASTAL WATERWAY

INDIAN RIVER

NETTLES
ISLAND

27°17.50'N
80°13.66'W

HERMAN'S BAY

A1A

W
S
N
E

Field Records

INTRACOASTAL WATERWAY

HERMAN'S BAY POINT

27°21.11'N
80°15.52'W

BIG MUD C

HUTCHINSON ISLAND NUCLEAR POWER PLANT

OLD HERMAN'S BAY

707

A1A

1 mile

Field Records

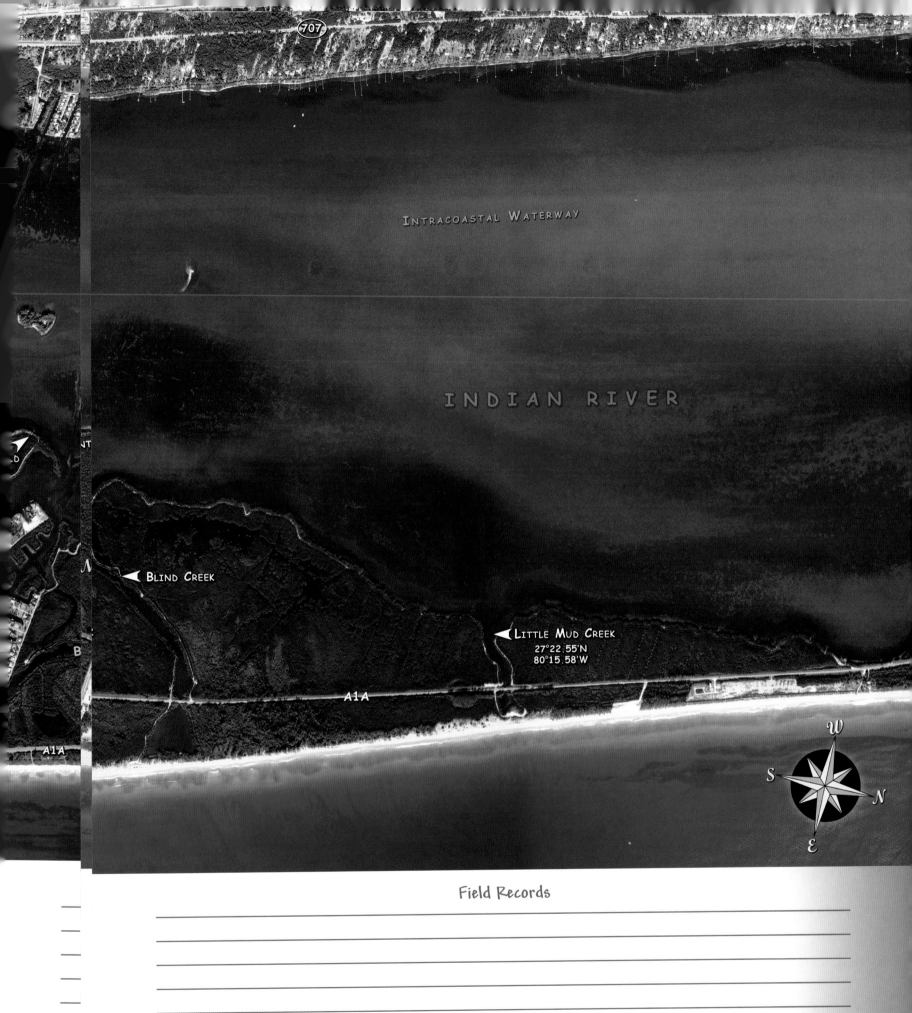

707

INTRACOASTAL WATERWAY

INDIAN RIVER

BLIND CREEK ◄

LITTLE MUD CREEK ◄
27°22.55'N
80°15.58'W

A1A

A1A

W
S · N
E

Field Records

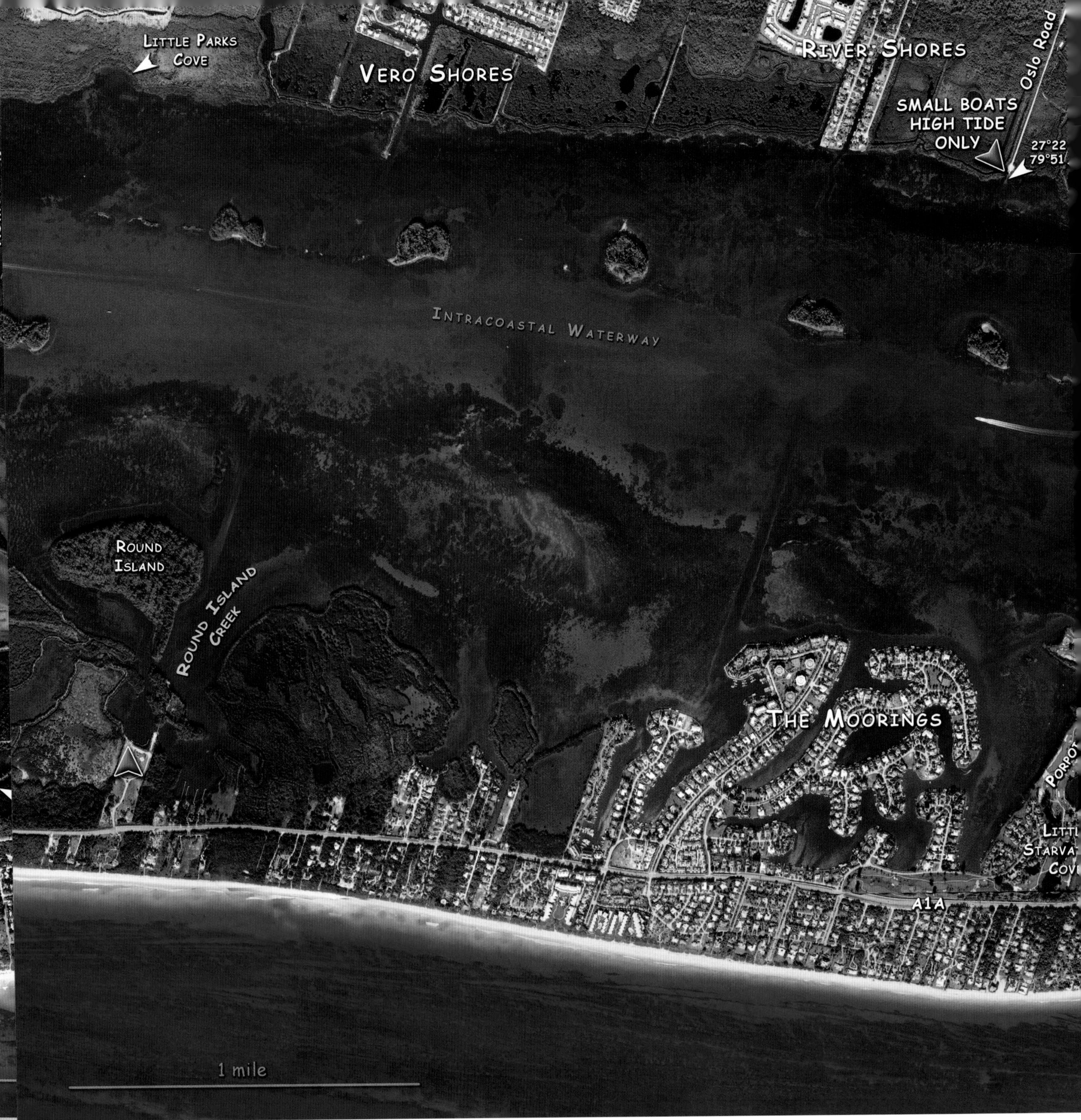

TAYL

Causeway

LITTLE PARKS
COVE

VERO SHORES

RIVER SHORES

Oslo Road

SMALL BOATS
HIGH TIDE
ONLY

27°22
79°51

INTRACOASTAL WATERWAY

ROUND
ISLAND

ROUND ISLAND CREEK

THE MOORINGS

PORPOI

LITTL
STARVA
COVE

A1A

1 mile

Field Records

VERO BEACH

CRAWFORD POINT

SOUTH RELIEF
CANAL

INTRACOASTAL WATERWAY

HELL'S
ISLAND

INDIAN RIVER

17TH STREET BRIDGE

PRANG ISLAND

PARADISE
ISLAND

27°37.90'N
80°21.80'W

DARK
POINT

ERWIN
COVE

A1A

RIOMAR

W

S   N

E

Field Records

_____

_____

_____

_____

_____

_____

_____

_____

VERO BEACH

17th Street Bridge
South Causeway

Intracoastal Waterway

60

North Causeway

Vossinbury Creek

Fritz Island

A1A

Bethel Creek

Riomar

27°38.85'N
80°22.05'W

Jandrew Cove

Giffo

W
S — N
E

1 mile

Field Records
_____
_____
_____
_____
_____
_____
_____
_____

GRAND HARBOR

27°40.65'N
80°22.98'W

INDIAN RIVER

GIFFORD POINT

GIFFORD ISLAND

INTRACOASTAL WATERWAY

SOUTH SISTER

BEE GUM POINT

POPLE POINT

STINGRAY CREEK

CHAMBERS COVE

JOHNS ISLAND

McCULLER COVE

JOHNS ISLAND CREEK

A1A

Field Records

US1

HOLE IN THE WALL ISLAND

NORTH SISTER

BARKER ISLAND (GEM ISLAND)

PINE ISLAND

SA
PO

27°40.48'N
80°20.79'W

INTRACOASTAL WATERWAY

A-1-A

1 mile

Field Records

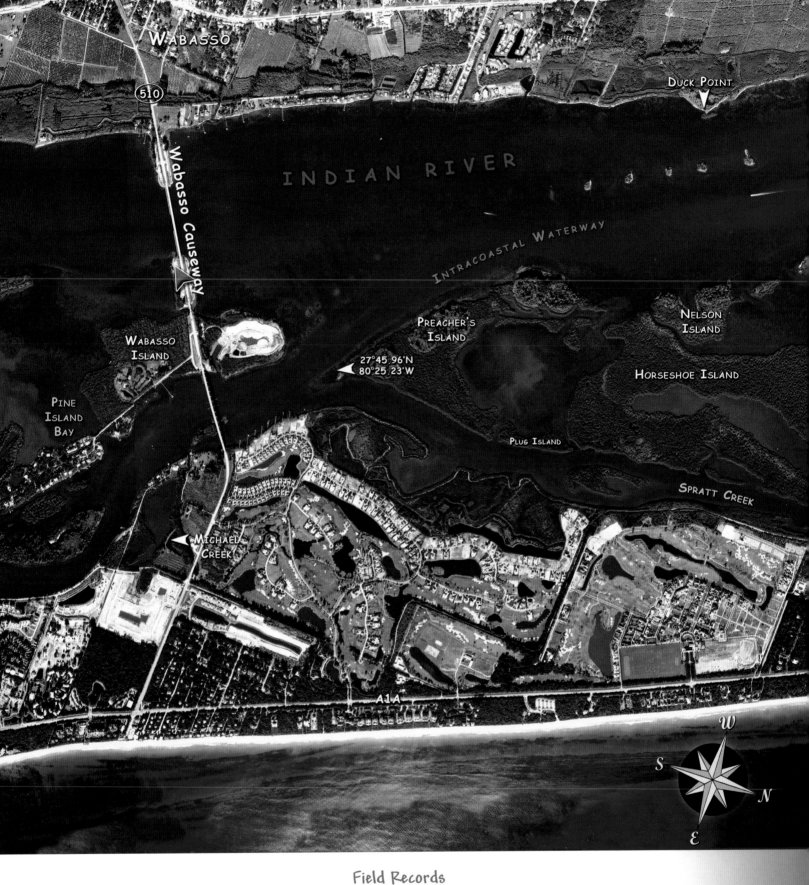

WABASSO

DUCK POINT

INDIAN RIVER

INTRACOASTAL WATERWAY

510

Wabasso Causeway

PREACHER'S
ISLAND

NELSON
ISLAND

27°45.96'N
80°25.23'W

HORSESHOE ISLAND

WABASSO
ISLAND

PINE
ISLAND
BAY

PLUG ISLAND

SPRATT CREEK

MICHAEL
CREEK

A1A

W

S

N

E

Field Records

US1

27°48.68'N
80°27.82'W

INTRACOASTAL WATERWAY

PAULS ISLAND

PELICAN ISLAND

ROOSEVELT ISLAND

ROSEATE ISLAND

SPRATT POINT

TURTLE PEN SLOUGH

BLACK POINT

COLLINS HOLE

W

S

N

E

BIG SLOUGH

A1A

1 mile

Field Records

_____

_____

_____

_____

_____

_____

_____

_____

EBASTIAN

St. Sebastian River

27°50.66'N
80°28.49'W

Intracoastal Waterway

INDIAN RIVER

Coconut Point ▷

Sebastian Inlet

Field Records

_____

_____

_____

_____

_____

_____

_____

PALM SHORES

US1

INTRACOASTAL WATERWAY

Pineda Causeway

404

MANGROVE POINT

MAGRUDER LAKE

3

1 mile

Field Records

PINEDA

PLOVER POINT

US1

INDIAN RIVER

INTRACOASTAL WATERWAY

MERRITT ISLAND

③

BANANA RIVER

W
S · E
N

Field Records

US1

COCOA

520

INTRACOASTAL WATERWAY

3

1 mile

Field Records

MAGNOLIA POINT

US1

528

INTRACOASTAL WATERWAY

INDIAN RIVER

MERRITT ISLAND

CANAVERAL BARGE CANAL

3

Field Records

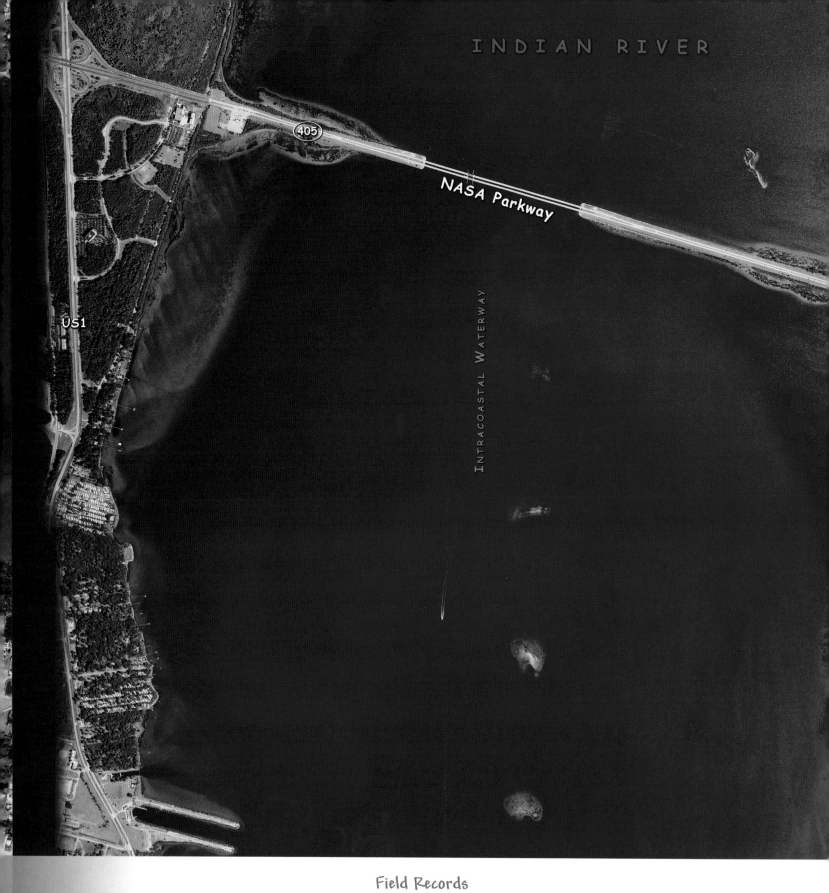

INDIAN RIVER

405

NASA Parkway

US1

INTRACOASTAL WATERWAY

Field Records

MOORE
POND

MERRITT ISLAND

405

PINE
ISLAND
CREEK

1 mile

N
W   E
S

Field Records

INTRACOASTAL WATERWAY

S1

ADDISON
POINT

INDIAN RIVER

Field Records

28°33.67'N
80°43.19'W

MOORE CREEK

MERRITT ISLAND

N
W   E
S

1 mile

Field Records

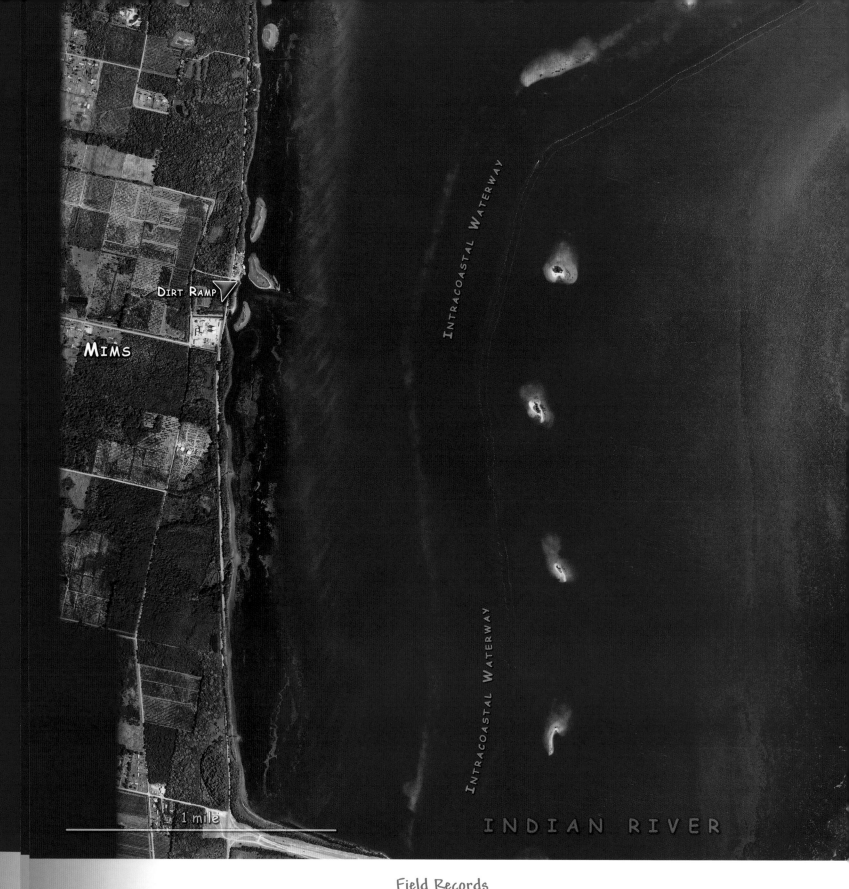

DIRT RAMP

MIMS

1 mile

INTRACOASTAL WATERWAY

INTRACOASTAL WATERWAY

INDIAN RIVER

Field Records

MARSH BAY

BLACK POINT

MERRITT ISLAND
NATIONAL WILDLIFE REFUGE

◄ BLACK POINT WILDLIFE DRIVE — GOOD BIRDING ►

28°40.06'N
80°46.96'W ►

N
W E
S
(406)

Field Records

_____
_____
_____
_____
_____
_____
_____
_____

28°42.71'N
80°50.01'W

1 mile

INTRACOASTAL WATERWAY

Field Records

N
W E
S

DUCKROOST COVE

DUCKROOST POINT
28°44.49'N
80°46.27'W

KENNEDY PARKWAY

HAULOVER CANAL

MERRITT ISLAND

INTRACOASTAL WATERWAY

DUMMIT COVE

Field Records

28°45.32'N
80°50.60'W
FLOUNDER CREEK

GRASSY POINT
28°45.78'N
80°48.86'W

1 mile

INDIAN RIVER

Field Records

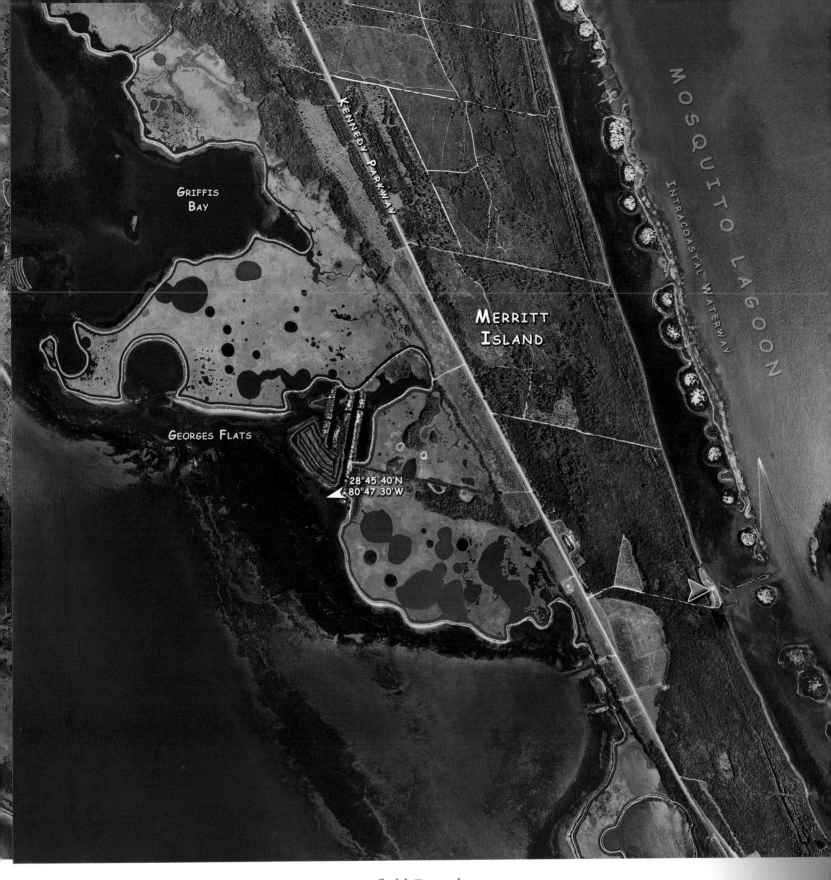

GRIFFIS BAY

KENNEDY PARKWAY

MERRITT ISLAND

MOSQUITO LAGOON

INTRACOASTAL WATERWAY

GEORGES FLATS

28°45.40'N
80°47.30'W

Field Records

INTRACOASTAL WATERWAY

Pineda Co

404

509

PALM SHORES

US1

IND

1 mile

Field Records

_____
_____
_____
_____
_____
_____
_____
_____

Field Records

_____
_____
_____
_____
_____
_____
_____

MERRITT ISLAND

INTRACOASTAL WATERWAY

HONEYMOON LAKE

BRADY ISLAND

GEORGE ISLAND

BAGGERS POINT

US1

③

INDIAN RIVER

1 mile

Field Records

BANANA RIVER

A1A

Field Records

PULLMAN POINT

BANANA

MERRITT
ISLAND

NEWFOUND HARBOR

HORTI
POINT

BUCK
POINT

INDIAN
RIVER

1 mile

3

Field Records

HOUSEBOAT CUT ➤

FLOWING WELL CUT

IVER

COCOA BEACH

JONES CREEK

SHORTY'S POCKET ➤

A1A

SNUG HARBOR

EDWARDS BAY

N
W E
S

Field Records

AUDUBON PARK

MILFORD POINT

MERRITT ISLAND

MERRITT ISLAND AIRPORT

NEWFOUND HARBOR

ANGLE CITY

3

1 mile

PULLMAN POINT

Field Records

BANANA RIVER

Cocoa Beach Causeway

520

Cocoa
Beach

Shell
Point

Thousand Islands

Big
Island

A1A

Houseboat Cut ▶

N
W · E
S

Field Records

_____

_____

_____

_____

_____

_____

_____

MERRITT ISLAND

CANAVERAL
BARGE CANAL

BENNETT CAUSEWAY

528

LONG POINT
28°22.98'N
80°39.65'W

BANANA RIVER

1 mile

Field Records

WEST
BASIN

MIDDLE
BASIN

401

PORT CANAVERAL

A1A

CAPE CANAVERAL

MIDDLE
BANK

HALL
ISLAND

N
W   E
S

Field Records

MERRITT ISLAND

MOTORBOATS PROHIBITED
FEDERAL MANATEE REFUGE

KARS
PARK
28°26.10'N
80°39.48'W

1 mile

Field Records

BANANA RIVER

MOTORBOATS PROHIBITED
FEDERAL MANATEE REFUGE

401

CANOE LAUNCH

WEST
BASIN

MIDDLE
BASIN

Field Records

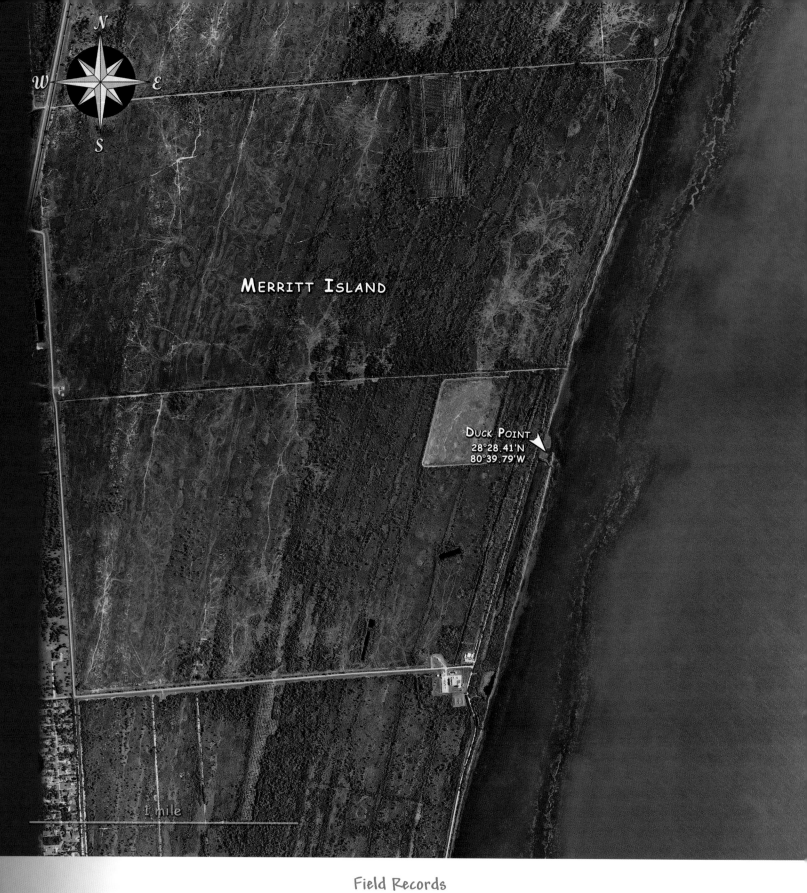

MERRITT ISLAND

DUCK POINT
28°28.41'N
80°39.79'W

1 mile

Field Records

_____
_____
_____
_____
_____
_____
_____
_____

BANANA RIVER

QUARTERMAN COVE

CACTUS POINT
28 28.47
80 35.68

MIDDLE POINT

HOME POINT

Field Records

W N E S

KENNEDY PARKWAY

MERRITT ISLAND

BUCK CREEK
(RESTRICTD AREA)
28°39.09'N
80°38.11'W

1 mile

Field Records

All Area Under and North of
NASA Parkway Restricted
NO ENTRY

405

NASA Parkway

White Point

BANANA RIVER

Field Records

MERRITT ISLAND

ALL AREA UNDER AND NORTH OF
NASA PARKWAY RESTRICTED
NO ENTRY

BANANA RIVER

1 mile

Field Records

JOHN F. KENNEDY
SPACE CENTER

LAUNCH COMPLEX

RESTRICTED AREA
NO ENTRY

Field Records

_____
_____
_____
_____
_____
_____
_____
_____

MAX HOECK
CREEK

1 mile

DIRT RAMP
SMALL BOATS
ONLY

Field Records

_____

_____

_____

_____

_____

_____

_____

_____

MERRITT ISLAND
NATIONAL WILDLIFE REFUGE

DIRT ROAD — GOOD BIRDING

MIDDLE
BANKS

PELICAN
ISLAND

MOSQUITO LAGOON

EDDY
CREEK

GALLINIPPER
POINT

Field Records

_____
_____
_____
_____
_____
_____
_____
_____

INDIAN
RIVER

MARSH BAY

DUNNIT CREEK

DIRT R.
SMALL BO
ONLY

W N E S

MERRITT ISLAND
NATIONAL WILDLIFE REFUGE

KENNEDY PARKWAY

1 mile

Field Records

CUCUMBER
ISLAND

DIRT ROAD — GOOD BIRDING

TURTLEPEN POINT
28°42.58'N
80°41.55'W

MOSQUITO LAGOON

Field Records

W N E S

MERRITT ISLAND

Intracoastal Waterway

DUCKROOST COVE

28°44.49'N
80°46.27'W

3

HAULOVER CANAL

INTRACOASTAL WATERWAY

INDIAN RIVER

KENNEDY PARKWAY

1 mile

Field Records

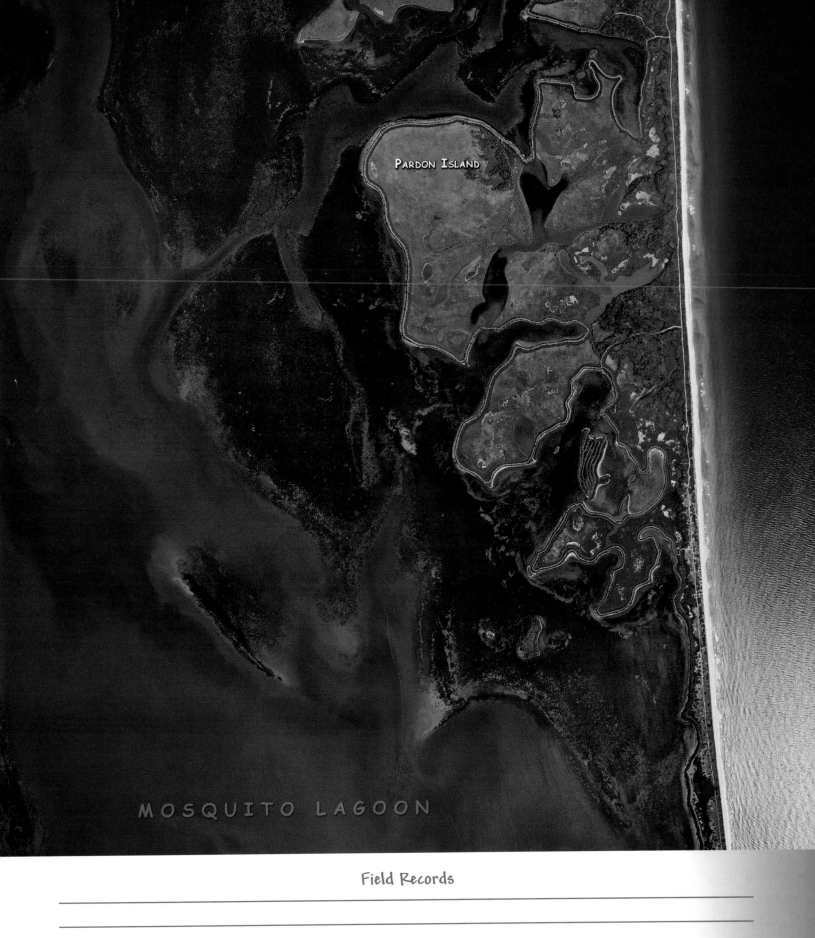

PARDON ISLAND

MOSQUITO LAGOON

Field Records

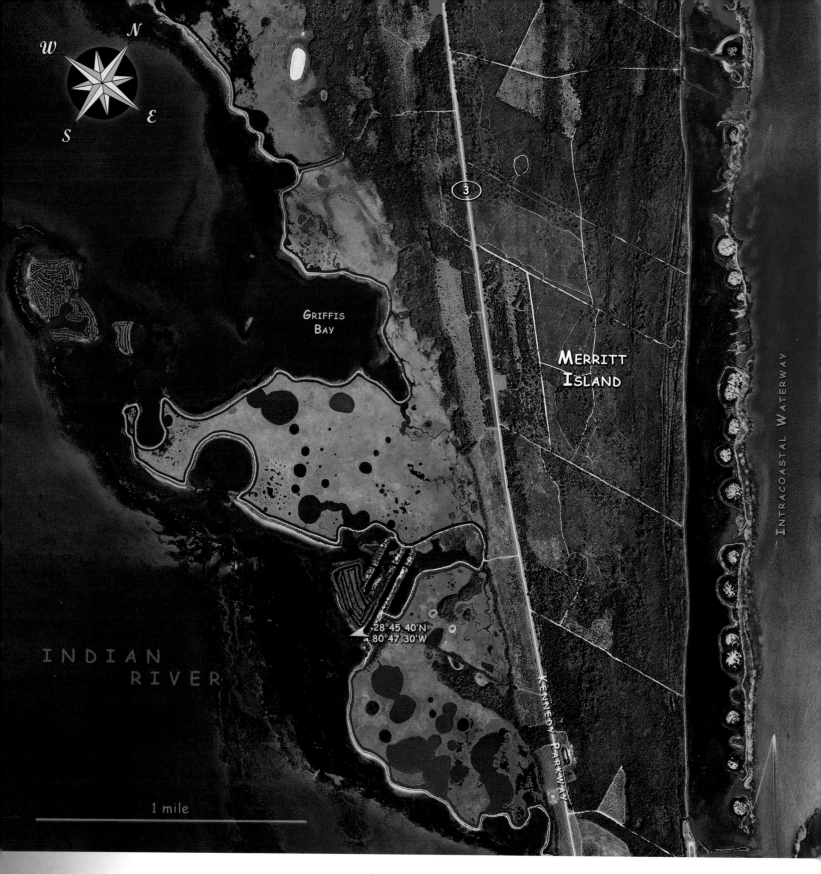

W N E S

GRIFFIS
BAY

MERRITT
ISLAND

INTRACOASTAL WATERWAY

28°45.40'N
80°47.30'W

INDIAN
RIVER

KENNEDY PARKWAY

3

1 mile

Field Records

MOSQUITO LAGOON

28°49.39'N
80°46.58'W

THREE CABBAGE
ISLAND

Field Records

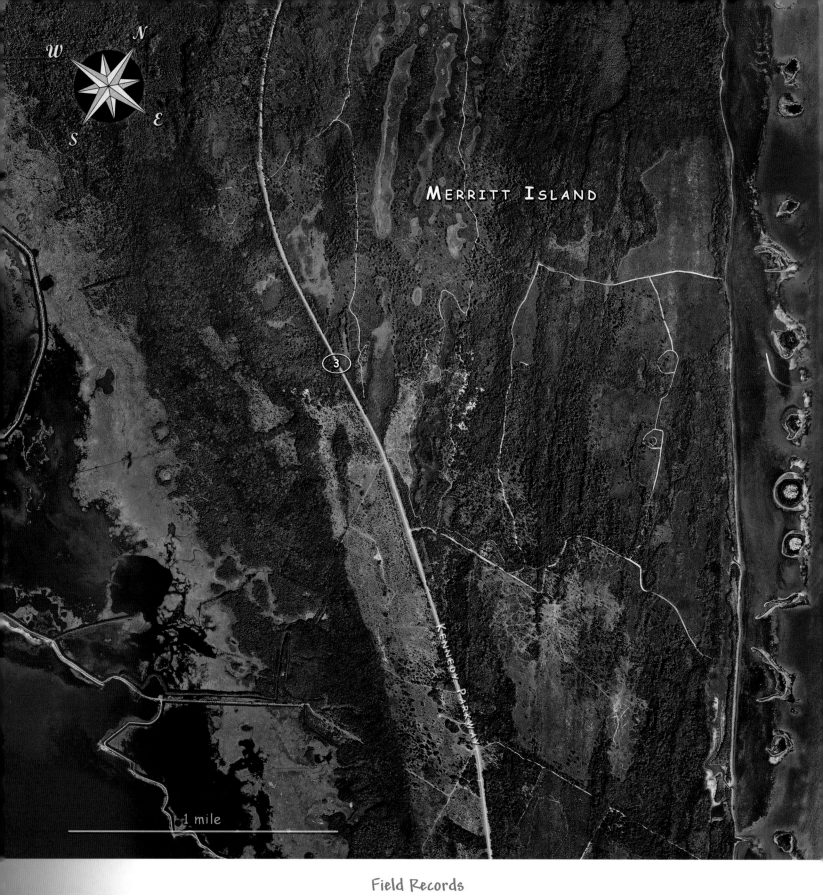

W N E S

MERRITT ISLAND

③

KENNEDY PARKWAY

1 mile

Field Records

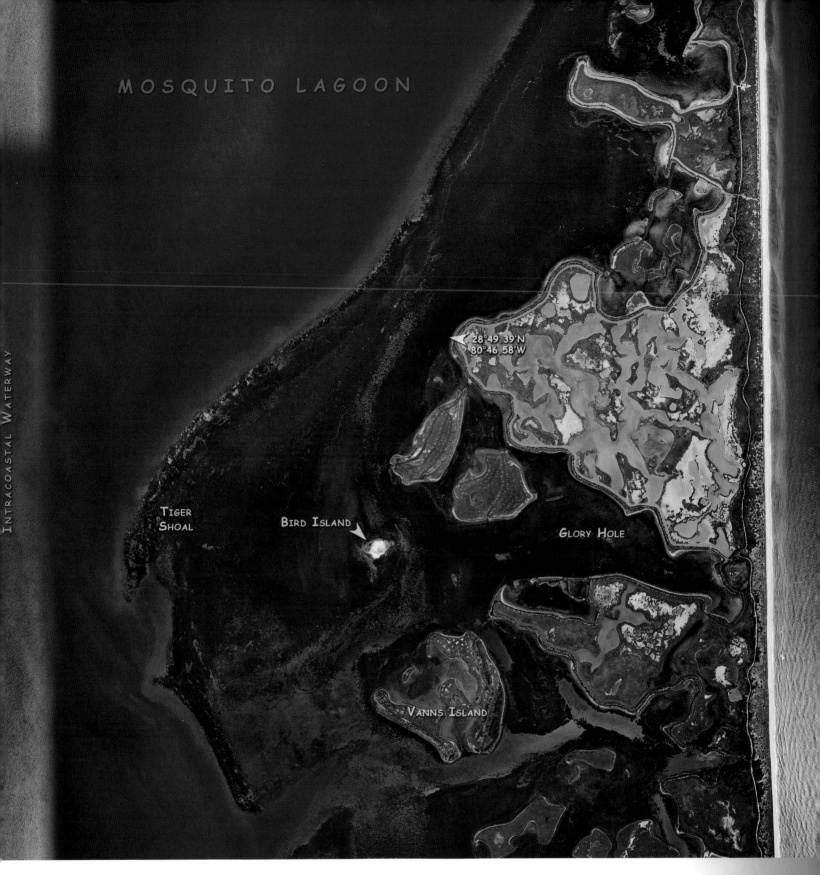

MOSQUITO LAGOON

INTRACOASTAL WATERWAY

28°49.39'N
80°46.58'W

TIGER
SHOAL

BIRD ISLAND

GLORY HOLE

VANNS ISLAND

Field Records

US1

MERRITT ISLAND

INTRACOASTAL WATERWAY

KENNEDY PARKWAY

1 mile

Field Records

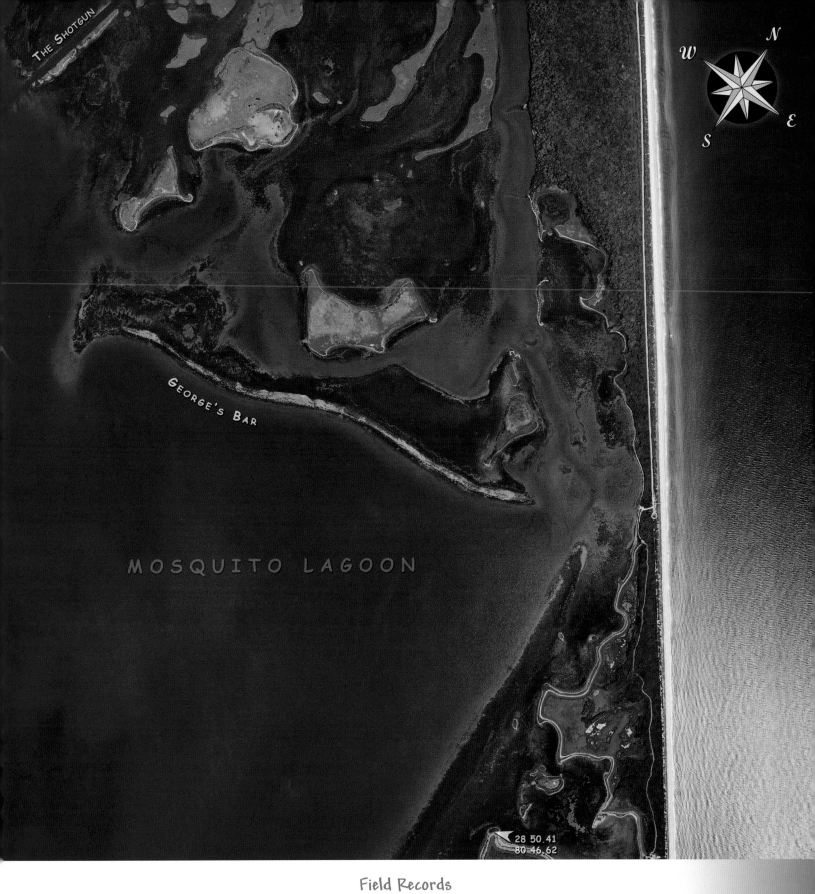

THE SHOTGUN

GEORGE'S BAR

MOSQUITO LAGOON

28 50.41
80 46.62

W N
E
S

Field Records

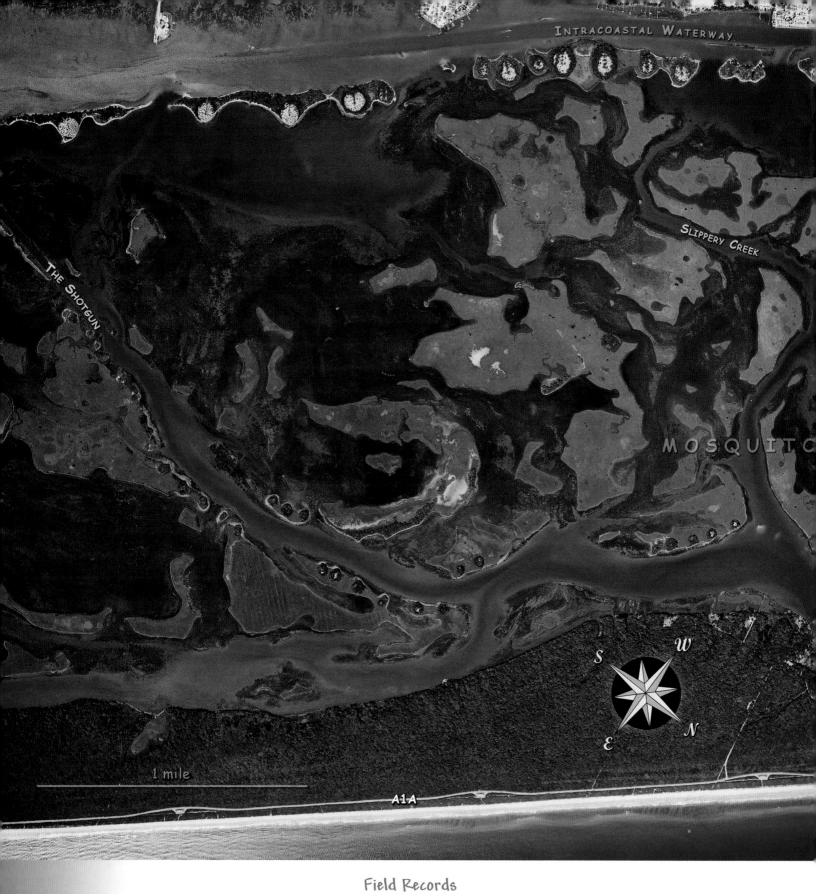

INTRACOASTAL WATERWAY

SLIPPERY CREEK

THE SHOTGUN

MOSQUITO

1 mile

A1A

Field Records

_____

_____

_____

_____

_____

_____

_____

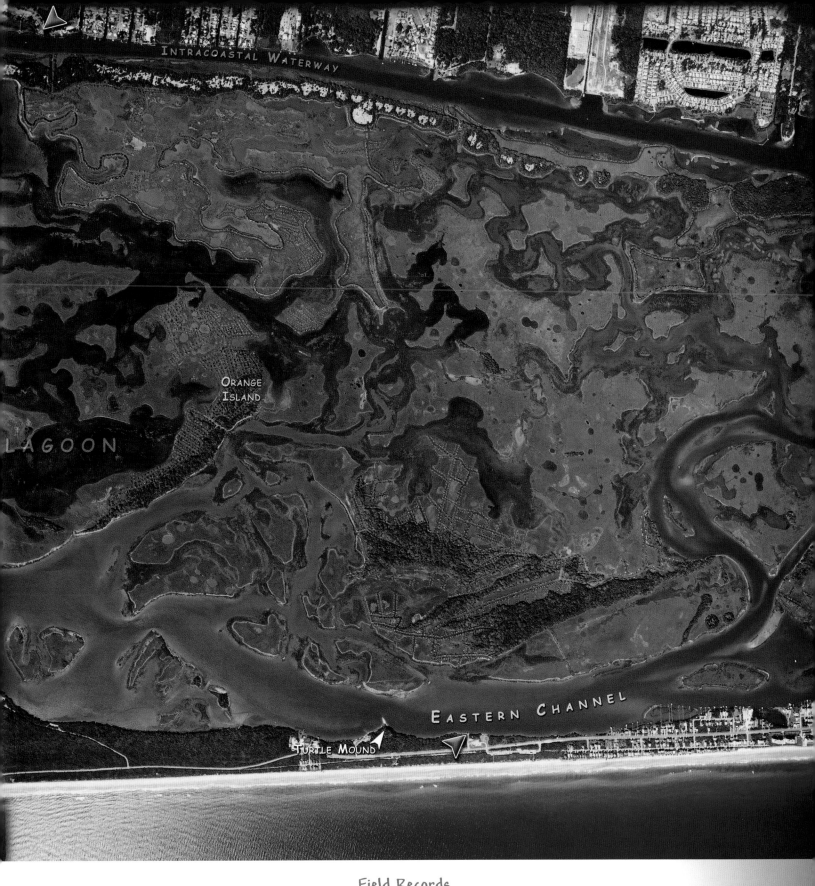

INTRACOASTAL WATERWAY

ORANGE ISLAND

LAGOON

EASTERN CHANNEL

TURTLE MOUND

Field Records

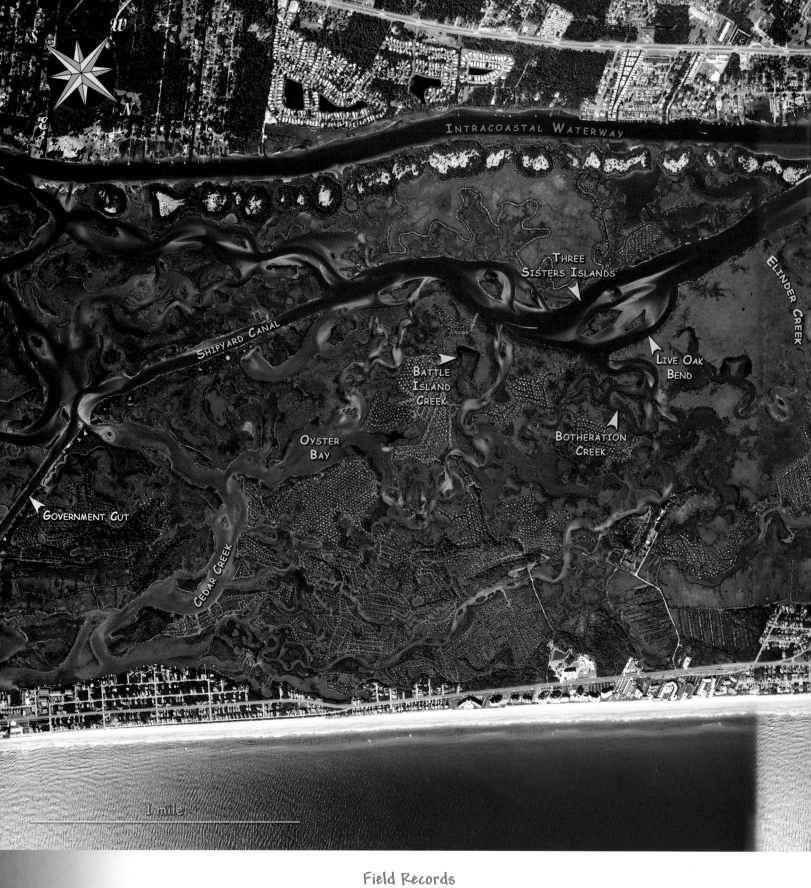

Field Records

Field Records

Callalisa Creek

Sheepshead Cut

Chicken Island

South Bridge Causeway

North Bridge Causeway

Intracoastal Waterway

Cook Creek

Smyr

New Smyrna Be

1 mile

Field Records

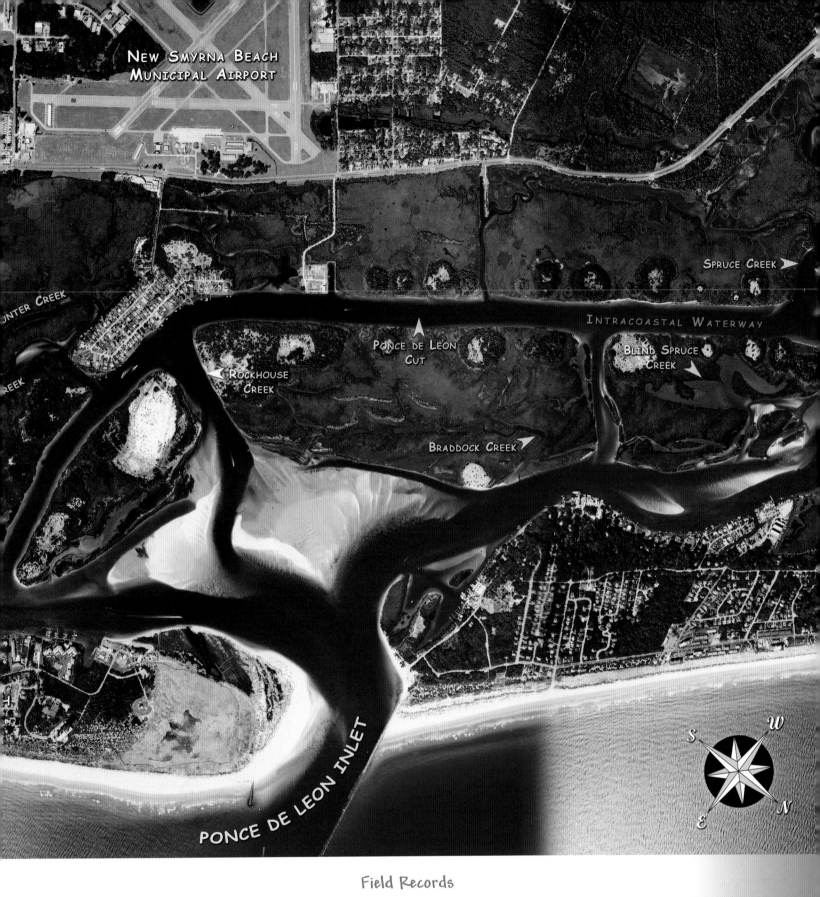

New Smyrna Beach Municipal Airport

Spruce Creek

Intracoastal Waterway

Ponce de Leon Cut

Rockhouse Creek

Blind Spruce Creek

Braddock Creek

Ponce de Leon Inlet

Field Records

Index to Common Names

Common Names (cont.)

INDEX TO LOCATIONS ON AERIAL PHOTOGRAPHS

Aerial Photograph Locations (cont.)

TO ORDER ADDITIONAL COPIES OF THIS BOOK AND OTHER TITLES:

WATERWAYS & BYWAYS OF THE INDIAN RIVER LAGOON

To order: send address accompanied by a check or bank draft in US dollars drawn on a US bank or an international postal money order in US dollars **for $55.00 plus an additional $5.00 for shipping and handling for USA orders** ($12.00 shipping and handling for international orders).

For credit card orders, please refer to zShops @ Amazon.com. Allow 3 weeks for delivery. Make checks payable to:

OffShore Graphics, Inc.
P.O. Box 6139
Washington, D.C. 20044-6139

CARIBBEAN REEF PLANTS: An Identification Guide to the Reef Plants of the Caribbean, Bahamas, Florida and Gulf of Mexico is a "user-friendly" identification guide to approximately 565 marine plants of the Caribbean Region. The book is richly illustrated with over 700 underwater photographs and 1,645 drawings. *Caribbean Reef Plants* allows divers, photographers and marine scientists to easily and accurately identify tropical Western Atlantic coral reef primary producers.

To order: send address accompanied by a check or bank draft in US dollars drawn on a US bank or an international postal money order in US dollars for $89.95 plus an additional $5.00 for shipping and handling for USA orders ($12.00 shipping and handling for international orders), to the above address.

SOUTH PACIFIC REEF PLANTS: A Divers' Guide to the Plant Life of South Pacific Coral Reefs is a "user-friendly" introduction to approximately 370 marine plants of the region with over 440 underwater photographs. These amazingly diverse plants are among the most photogenic and spectacularly colorful of coral-reef organisms. Specialized terminology has been kept to a minimum to facilitate use by divers, naturalists, reef managers and scientists in other disciplines.

To order: send address accompanied by a check or bank draft in US, dollars drawn on a US bank or an international postal money order in US dollars for $45.00 plus an additional $5.00 for shipping and handling for USA orders ($12.00 shipping and handling for international orders), to the above address.

---

website: www.erols.com/offshoregraphics/   e-mail: offshoregraphics@starpower.net